P9-DYY-446

FRÉDÉRIC JOLIOT-CURIE

The Man and His Theories

by Pierre Biquard

TRANSLATED BY GEOFFREY STRACHAN

A FAWCETT PREMIER BOOK

Fawcett Publications, Inc., Greenwieh, Conn.

MEMBER OF AMERICAN BOOK PUBLISHERS COUNCIL

Library of Congress Catalog Card Number: 65-24212
First Fawcett Premier printing, December 1966

Published by Fawcett World Library,
67 West 44th Street, New York, N. Y. 10036
Printed in the United States of America

AUTHOR'S ACKNOWLEDGMENT

THIS study could not have been completed without the co-operation of numerous people, to whom I should like to express here my most sincere thanks to:

Mme. Hélène Langevin, M. Pierre Joliot, M. and Mme. Charles Lapique, M. Georges Léon, and also MM. J. Adnet, J. D. Bernal, E. M. S. Burhop, Dr. Boyadjiev, L. Casanova, M. and Mme. F. Cohen, M. and Mme. Courtillot, Mme. E. Cotton, M. L. Denivelle, H.R.H. Queen Elisabeth of the Belgians, MM. W. Gentner, S. A. Goudsmit, P. Kitrosser, L. Kowarski, J. Lafitte, R. Mayer, R. Michaut, H. Moureu, F. Netter, W. A. Noyes, B. Pontecorvo, Lord Russell, P. Savel, D. Skobeltsyn, G. Teisser, F. Vigne, P. Villon, E. Wellhoff, J. Wyart.

TRANSLATOR'S ACKNOWLEDGMENT

MY thanks are due to Dr. Martin Gregory, whose help in preparing this English edition has been invaluable. G. S.

Contents

SELECTED WRITINGS

CONTENTS

1

The Nobel Prize[1]

On November 14, 1935, at the house which he recently
had had built at 76 Avenue Le Notre in the Parc de Sceaux,
Paris, Frédéric Joliot opened a telegram he had just received.
It did not come as a complete surprise, because for several
months his colleagues had kept him and his wife in their confidence. Nevertheless, it was with some emotion that he read:

I HAVE THE HONOR TO INFORM YOU THAT THE ACADEMY
OF SCIENCES OF SWEDEN HAS AWARDED THE NOBEL PRIZE
FOR CHEMISTRY OF 1935 TO YOU AND MADAME CURIE-
JOLIOT LETTER FOLLOWS=

SIGNED PLEIJEL SECRETARY PER

Laying down on his desk the blue slip of paper on which
was written a change in his destiny, he glanced at the upper
part of his glass-fronted bookshelf, where the collection of
blue "Nobel" volumes inherited from Marie Curie was
ranged. . . .

He tried to recall again the list of names to which those
of himself and his wife would be added and he did not
forget that—uniquely—that of Marie Curie figured there on
two occasions, in 1903 and in 1911.

Various starting points could have been chosen to introduce the rich but all too brief existence of Frédéric Joliot:
his birth on March 19, 1900; his entry into Marie Curie's
laboratory in October, 1925; his marriage with Irène Curie
on October 4, 1926; the discovery of the fission of uranium
in 1938; the starting up of ZOE in 1948. But it was above
all the time when he was awarded the Nobel Prize that
seemed the most suitable, because the discovery of artificial
radioactivity, both in itself and in its repercussions on the

[1] A glossary of technical terms which might be unfamiliar to
the nonspecialist reader is given at the end of the book.

lives of these two scientists, marked a turning point of great significance.

This point was made by M. Louis de Broglie, the permanent secretary of the Académie des Sciences, in the account of the life and work of Frédéric Joliot that he gave on December 14, 1959, at the annual "awards" session of the Académie:

Their reputation as physicists had become international but they had yet to make a great discovery which they could call their own. This great discovery, which was the fruit of the fine work they had been doing, was that of artificially radioactive elements.

And a little further on, speaking this time only of Joliot:

Suddenly plunged into the bright limelight (too bright perhaps for those who love work and research) of great scientific celebrity, he was to see a rapid development in his career and to know the satisfaction and the burden of honors and responsibilities.

This fame in no way affected the simple integrity of the man but it quickly made him develop a profound awareness of his responsibilities as a scientist and a citizen and it led him to make choices that would mark his destiny.

In order to take part in the ceremony of the distribution of the Nobel Prizes, the two young French scientists went to Stockholm. It was Joliot's first visit. Irène had been there once before with her mother in 1911.

The celebrations, in the midst of which the presentation of prizes takes place, on December 10, put the Swedish capital in a ferment. Well before the appointed hour there is a crowd thronging around the "Palace of Concerts." The King and the Royal Family are present at the distribution of the prizes, surrounded by members of the government and the diplomatic corps. The ceremonies take place according to the strictest protocol but in an atmosphere of cordiality.

I should like to evoke for you now some memories of that journey, when I made contact with the Scandinavian people for the first time—the impression of freshness and honesty, of youth and straightforwardness which I retained. In particular there was a procession of students at a celebration at the town hall in Stockholm which left me with a dazzling and unforgettable vision of health and vigor.[2]

---

[2] Joliot recalled these impressions in a broadcast on the French radio in April, 1940, at the moment when Nazi Germany was attacking Norway.

Two days later the Prize winners found themselves in the much less formal setting of the lecture hall of Stockholm University. The audience consisted of a number of foreign scholars, the members of the Nobel foundation, and a great number of Swedish academics.

The Joliot-Curies heard the British physicist James Chadwick telling of the discovery of the neutron, a discovery toward which the two of them had also made a great contribution.

Then Irène Curie was called on to speak. She described the first experiments in which new radioactive elements were produced by nuclear reactions. Remembering, no doubt, the many times when people had tried to attribute more importance to Marie Curie than to Pierre Curie, and in order to avoid any misunderstanding, she explained:

These experiments were carried out by Monsieur Joliot and myself, working together, and the way in which we have divided up this lecture is simply for convenience.

This short sentence expressed with the rigorous terseness of the scientist the double fact of total collaboration and of a full and confident union between the two scientists.

When his wife had finished speaking Frédéric Joliot picked up several sheets of paper and went to the blackboard to continue:

The interpretation of our first experiments rested, as Mme. Joliot-Curie has just shown, upon facts of a purely physical nature.

The young French physicist, with brown hair and bright eyes, elegant and athletic in appearance, aged thirty-five but looking hardly more than thirty, delivered his lecture in clear and measured tones. He explained how in the course of several months it had been possible to add more than fifty new radioactive elements to the thirty naturally radioactive ones already present in the earth's crust.

There was a brief pause as his eyes left his notes and rested on his wife for a moment. Then he continued, with ill-concealed emotion:

It was certainly a great satisfaction for our late lamented teacher, Marie Curie, to see the list of radioactive elements which, in the company of Pierre Curie, she had the honor to inaugurate, extended in this way.

All those present pictured Pierre and Marie Curie for a moment. For their daughter Irène and for Frédéric Joliot the memory was richer, deeper, and more lasting.

Frédéric Joliot drew to the end of his lecture. He described the current stage that he and his wife had reached in their research. Then he paused again and turned to the future. In the same tone as he had used to describe experiments and formulate theories, he allowed his creative imagination to indulge in prophecies—prophecies which seemed bold in 1935 but which, thanks to him, were to become reality in 1938.

From the sum of the observed facts, we understand that the several hundred different types of atoms which constitute our planet should not be considered as having been created once and for all time. We observe them because they have survived. Other less stable ones have disappeared. It is probably some of these "vanished" atoms which have been re-created in the laboratory. Hitherto it has only been possible to obtain atoms which have a relatively short life, extending from a fraction of a second to several months. In order to create an appreciable quantity of an element with a much longer life, it would be necessary to have at one's disposal an extremely intense source of nuclear radiation. Is there any hope of realizing this new dream?

If we look back at the past and consider the progress made by science at an ever increasing pace, we may feel entitled to believe that researchers, building up or breaking down elements at will, will be able to bring about nuclear reactions of an explosive nature—veritable chemical chain reactions. If such reactions come to be propagated in matter, one can imagine the enormous release of useful energy which will take place. But, alas, if all the elements on our planet are contaminated, we can only look forward with apprehension to the consequences of the unleashing of such a cataclysm. Astronomers sometimes observe how a star of mediocre brilliance, which is ordinarily invisible to the naked eye, suddenly increases in size and becomes very bright and visible without the aid of instruments—this is the apparition of a supernova. It may be that this sudden inflammation of the star is caused by these explosive chain reactions—a process which researchers will no doubt try to bring about, while taking, let us hope, the necessary precautions.

This text was not improvised on the platform by an orator who had allowed himself to be carried away by his subject. It was composed in advance and every one of the terms used was carefully considered. It was delivered in December,

1935, and in 1938, only three years later, the German chemists Otto Hahn and Fritz Strassmann discovered the fission of uranium.

The new phenomena which he and Irène Joliot-Curie had just described, together with the equivalence of mass and energy established by Einstein and Langevin, made this vision of the future possible for Joliot.

At the same time he saw in it certain dangers. In the light of our knowledge today the perils he had evoked that day in Stockholm do not seem likely to threaten our planet. But other dangers were later to be discovered. In the fight against these he was to dedicate a considerable part of his life.

In the same place, thirty-two years before, Pierre Curie had ended his own Nobel Prize lecture. Frédéric and Irène Joliot-Curie had read and reread the text:[3]

One may imagine how in criminal hands radium could become very dangerous, and one has the right to ask at this stage if it is to the advantage of humanity to discover the secrets of nature—if we are mature enough to profit by them or if this knowledge will not be harmful to us. The example of Nobel's own discoveries is characteristic: high explosives have given men the means to perform admirable works. They are also a terrible means of destruction in the hands of the great criminals who involve peoples in war. I am one of those people who think, like Nobel, that humanity will derive more good than harm from new discoveries.

In August, 1945, the "terrible means of destruction" wrought its grim work on the Japanese towns of Hiroshima and Nagasaki. In 1950 Frédéric Joliot-Curie was to go to Stockholm once more, to take part in the work of the World Peace Council, of which he was the prime mover and the president. Thus forty-seven years after Pierre Curie had given his warning, and fifteen years after his own Nobel prize lecture, Joliot launched the "Stockholm Appeal" which marked a decisive moment in the mobilization of the will of humanity against the dangers of atomic weapons.

The Swedish capital seems to have been destined to be the scene of the principal stages in a life that was devoted to science and to humanity.

[3] See Pierre Curie's Nobel lecture and also Marie Curie's admirable book, *Pierre Curie* (Payot, 1923; Denoel, 1955).

2

His Early Life

JEAN-FRÉDÉRIC JOLIOT[1] was born in Paris on March 19, 1900, in a little town house in the sixteenth arrondissement. His father was then fifty-seven and his mother forty-nine. He was the youngest of six children. Two of his brothers died young. His brother Henri was to be killed in the course of the first engagements of the First World War. He had two sisters, Jeanne, his senior by seventeen years, and Marguerite, a talented painter with a gay and bohemian temperament.

At the age of ten he was sent to boarding school at the Lycée Lakanal in Sceaux. At the end of his year in the eighth class* he was called before the "Conseil de Discipline" to be given the "Congratulations of the Conseil de Classe." He continued his studies in a most satisfactory manner, as is shown by his school reports, which his mother carefully preserved, although in them one may note his masters' repeated complaints about his weakness in French and his shortcomings in spelling.

At that time he was chiefly interested in sports and he devoted no more time than was absolutely necessary to schoolwork. He was good at games, particularly at football. Later on he was fond of recalling that he had played in a big match at Amiens. There is, indeed, among his school reports a cutting from an Amiens newspaper, yellow with age. In an article about the forthcoming encounter between the Amiens Athletic Club and the Association Sportive Française, the sports commentator, using the conventional pseudonym of "SHOOT," wrote:

> Inside left: Joliot. Has been playing next to his center forward for three years. Always a threat to the opponent's goal.

[1] Very early on his second Christian name came to be the only one used.

* *Translator's Note:* In French schools the first class is the most senior; boys in the eighth class would be aged about eleven.

Frédéric was not a particularly well-behaved child—quite the contrary—and later on he often admitted: "I caused my poor mother a great deal of worry, particularly when I went shopping with her and stole the fruit and sweets which were on display."

There was one incident from that period of his life which made a great impression on him. It introduced him to— and made him hate and fear—the sudden madness of violence.

At that time he must have been fourteen or fifteen. One day he was leaving the Lycée Lakanal to return home when a milk boy began to abuse him. He did not reply. The boy became bolder and his remarks grew more offensive. Then, doubtless annoyed at the lack of reaction, he began to throw stones at him. Frédéric turned suddenly, took hold of the boy and knocked him down. The boy's head struck the pavement several times. Although no serious injury resulted, Joliot was always to remember how he got into a state of blind fury which increased with each thud of the boy's head banging against the ground.

Joliot's father's business was quite prosperous and was entrusted to a manager, so that he was able to devote his leisure to his favorite amusements—shooting, fishing, and music. He often took his young son with him. These long walks through the forest, the time spent hiding behind cover, and the periods of waiting on a fishing boat before dawn gave Frédéric his knowledge and love of nature. From an early age he was gifted with exceptional powers of observation and perception in the pursuit of game and fish.

It was on shooting and fishing expeditions with my father that I learned to lose myself in nature, and to be receptive to all the ways in which animals, plants, and the country reveal themselves. I would know by instinct: here there are fish, there, game; near here we shall find a stream; at this hour the pheasants are over there.[2]

Later on he became an excellent shot and fisherman—not surprisingly, as he managed to excel in everything he did.

In conversation with many friends he often discussed the origin of his love of these two sports—both of which are in truth somewhat cruel. He saw in his love the persistence of man's ancestral struggle to satisfy his vital needs. He was shocked by the mere idea of killing an animal other

[2] *Frédéric Joliot-Curie* by Michel Rouzé, Editeurs Français Réunis, p. 51.

than for food, and he could not have pressed the trigger
of his rifle in such a case. Once, much later, he even found
himself unable to do so when his target was eminently
edible. He was stalking game in Arcouest one summer's day
in 1955. He experienced intensely these moments, when his
senses were on the alert and he was aware of the smallest
sounds and movements. Suddenly he noticed a bird, a female, within range of his rifle. It had heard nothing and
was completely without suspicion as Joliot took aim while
continuing to watch it. The bird was preoccupied with one
of its babies. . . .

It was there at the end of my rifle; I followed it for several
moments but I could not shoot . . . the old hunter in me was
overcome. . . .

Frédéric Joliot's father played the French hunting horn
with passion and talent. Two magnificent horns had been
left to him by the Count of Champigny, in whose honor
he had composed a horn-call named after him, which has
remained famous. These two horns hung in the dining room
of the Joliots' flat, before being moved to the dining room
of the Joliot-Curie house at Antony. And when Frédéric Joliot
was showing them to a visitor he would always add: "And
my father could play high G on them!"

Shooting, fishing, music were not the only fields in which
his father had an influence on the sixth of his children.
Before becoming a prosperous businessman Henri Joliot
had been a soldier. He was called up during the war of 1870
(at the age of twenty-seven) and took an active part in the
"Paris Commune," after which he was forced to leave the
country until an amnesty was declared. The young Frédéric often heard his father talking about the events of that period—
the collaboration between the "Versailles Party" and the Prus-
sians, the repression, the executions, the escape to Belgium
through the enemy lines. It was then that he was most
proud of his father, at the same time as he began to
acquire a profound sense of the tragedy of that historical
episode. It may seem strange that this was a frequent subject
in their sheltered home when his father had many years
before given up all militant activity. But it was here that
the great influence of his mother intervened. Emilie Joliot,
née Roederer, came from an Alsatian family. Her father
had been sauce-cook to Napoleon III, and as such, he was
the only servant permitted to be present at the emperor's
meals and, quite frequently, to converse with him. Although

Emilie loved to recount her memories of these meals, she was nonetheless profoundly republican and, even when she was living in Alsace, she had much astonished the people of her milieu by not refusing to have social intercourse with Jewish families. She retained the austere manner and appearance of her deeply Protestant background but she was fundamentally liberal. Her great good nature and deep sense of justice had a profound influence on Frédéric, her last-born, throughout her life and indeed after her death.

Joliot told Michel Rouzé about his childhood memories:

" 'Thus,' recounted Frédéric Joliot, 'I was brought up in a kind of bourgeois existence but I was sharply aware of the contrast between this way of life and my father's memories of the Commune and the things my mother told me. . . .' "

He was not surprised to be given, like the other sons of the middle class, an education designed to secure "a good job" later on. But he felt that his own comfortable existence was somehow out of step with the heroic youth of his father. He was surprised to realize that, as he had grown older, his father had lost his will to fight. Why did he not continue the social struggle?

Sometimes Henri Joliot went off for a short trip to his native region of France and took his son with him:

"It was among the workers of the east that I saw my father become his old self again. I felt that at bottom he had remained a working man and when he was with middle-class people he was to some extent playing a part."

Madame Joliot tended to reproach her husband for this change. She was the one who kept the flame of militancy burning in the family, ignoring his father's shrugging shoulders. "Leave the children in peace!" he would say to his wife. "Great heavens, didn't I have enough trouble of that kind!"[3]

The death of Frédéric Joliot's father and changes in the family fortunes caused the Joliots to leave the wealthy sixteenth arrondissement of Paris and to set up housekeeping near the "Lion de Belfort" on the fifth floor of the block of apartments at 4 Avenue du General-Leclerc* (in those days

---

[3] *Ibid,* p. 24.

*Translator's Note: In the Montparnasse quarter—the fourteenth arrondissement. The "Lion de Belfort" is a statue in the Place Denfert-Rocherlau, a replica of the statue at Belfort, a symbol of the Paris Commune.

called the Avenue d'Orléans). The apartment was huge and was surrounded by a large balcony that overlooked the Avenue and the Rue Daguerre. The Lycée Lakanal had been abandoned in favor of the municipal École Primaire Supérieure Lavoisier, where the young man studied for the entrance examinations for the École Municipale de Physique et de Chimie Industrielles de la Ville de Paris where the courses were free.

To the despair of his mother, Frédéric Joliot's room as a student was not always perfectly tidy. On the big worktable there was a bit of everything, notably a wireless telegraph receiving set which he had knocked together as an amateur. But it was particularly in the field of chemistry that the young man liked to make experiments, and the dressing room next to his bedroom bore the traces on the walls and on the floor of some particularly successful experiments. One could also see, affixed to the wall, a framed page from *Lectures pour tous:* a portrait of Pierre and Marie Curie in their laboratory. . . .

As a child I read in magazines the wonderful story of the discovery of radium by Pierre and Marie Curie. This discovery took place at the École de Physique et de Chimie. I remember cutting out a photograph of the two scientists and fixing it up in the room I had converted into a little chemistry laboratory, which will be well known to some of my friends here tonight.[4]

The future engineer and physicist was also interested in applied aerodynamics. He never failed to demonstrate to his visitors the effectiveness with which his blowpipe sent paper pellets into the glasses of people sitting on the terrace of the big café on the other side of the Avenue d'Orléans. Close friends were taken to the part of the balcony overlooking the Rue Daguerre and shown a half-open window on the third floor of the apartment buildings opposite. "Several messages, transmitted by means of this instrument here, have been completely successful in pleading my cause with the charming girl who lives in that room!"

Apart from the radio set, the blowpipe and a blackboard, there was also a large cupboard in Joliot's room. On the

---

[4] From a speech made by F. Joliot-Curie on January 11, 1936, on the occasion of the dinner held for him and Irène Joliot-Curie by the École de Physique et de Chimie, the Faculty of Science at the University of Paris, and various scientific societies.

inside surfaces of the two large wooden doors, as well as on the front of the drawers, were stuck pieces of paper on which were written, in his mother's hand, precepts which she considered very important: "A place for everything and everything in its place"; "Never put off till tomorrow what you can do today," etc.

Joining in the game, Joliot one day added the celebrated motto of William of Orange, which he had cut out of a magazine: "It is not necessary to have hope in order to undertake an enterprise, nor to be successful in order to persevere."

If Frédéric still caused his mother some concern in regard to tidiness, he had nonetheless, from that period, already imposed upon himself a strict discipline for his laboratory experiments: that of keeping a notebook and writing down all his observations in it scrupulously and chronologically.

The notebooks Joliot thus accumulated during the course of his life are numerous, and their historical interest varies considerably, since they contain his notes as a young student on certain exercises at the School of Artillery at Poitiers, notes on the tides and the wind off Bréhat, and notes on the starting of the first French atomic pile. But one notices omissions: in moments of exaltation at the great discoveries the notes were made on loose sheets of paper.

At the end of the First World War Joliot began the last and most important phase of his studies. In July, 1918, he took the entrance examination for the École de Physique et de Chimie, and failed.

Joliot was accepted after the examination in 1919, but ill health forced him to interrupt his studies and it was finally not until October, 1920, that he entered the school with the thirty-ninth intake. The director was the chemist Albin Haller and the director of studies was the physicist Paul Langevin.

At the end of the first three terms Joliot, like all his fellow students, had to choose between the options of physics and chemistry. At first he chose the second, and it was only at the last minute that he changed his mind.[5] So when he arrived, after all the others, to hand in his apparatus to Gustave Bémont—who, with Pierre and Marie Curie had

[5] It was the fact that we both took the same decision at the same time, though quite independently, that crystallized the friendship between Joliot and myself.

isolated radium and who personified for his students the gruff but deeply good-natured alchemist—he was greeted by a remark he never forgot: "Here is the physicist from the second brew!"

Joliot, whose cleverness in experimenting manifested itself right from the start of the practical classes, rapidly established himself as the best student of his year and ended up as "major" of it. This status brought him into contact with the director of studies on a number of occasions. These visits were a trial for him, for he was deeply impressed by this teacher, whose lectures on electricity were a revelation to all his pupils: "I would knock on the door," he liked to recount, "the 'Chief's' limpid eyes would be fixed on me—and I would completely forget why I had come to see him."

All those who have been privileged to be taught by Paul Langevin at the École de Physique et de Chimie, at the École Normale at Sèvres, or at the Collège de France have been more or less affected by it. For Frédéric Joliot this experience was absolutely decisive, for a number of reasons we shall have occasion to examine. Unconsciously he borrowed from the man he loved, admired, and venerated as his master a number of characteristic tricks and attitudes, such as moving his hand slowly backward and forward over his hair or leaving the blackboard to make a white mark with the chalk on the radiator for emphasis. Happily the resemblance between their lectures went beyond these gestures. Frédéric Joliot had learned the lesson from his master that one must at all costs make the audience, especially if it is composed of beginners, feel that science is something living. One must convey the value and importance of what has already been achieved, while making them realize that everyone can make his original contribution to the edifice which is being constructed.

Langevin also influenced Joliot at that time in quite a different area of thought. In the year 1920, in the autumn of which he entered the École de Physique et de Chimie, there were bitter political and social struggles. On two occasions, in the case of the big strikes and that of the trial of the Black Sea sailors, Joliot found answers to the questions which troubled him in the great scientist's declarations.

In the spring of 1920 a general strike of transport workers had broken out. In order to check the trade unions the government had arranged for the creation of the "Civic

Union" which recruited strikebreakers, mainly from among the students. The attraction of a new and temporary occupation, the appeal of free first-class travel on the trains, and the social background of the students made this recruiting very easy. However there was some resistance, particularly at the École de Physique et de Chimie. The school administration wanted to stop the lectures in order to allow the students to enroll in the Civic Union. A group of pupils wrote about this to the director of studies. In reply he wrote an open letter which was published in the newspaper *L'Humanité* on May 18, 1920:

. . . I am equally convinced of my duty to give you my firm opinion on the situation which has been created for students at technical schools by the introduction of conflicts in which these young men find themselves obliged to take sides before they are old enough to do so. As yet they know nothing of this world of industrial work which they are to enter, and where their present attitude may later create great difficulties for them. Our duty must be to see that the schools are not diverted from their normal activity. . . .

The voice of a teacher of science raised against the attempts to arouse class hatred struck a chord in the hearts of many young people and in particular that of Frédéric Joliot.

On December 6 of the same year Paul Langevin for the first time publicly supported the plea for an amnesty for the Black Sea sailors and for André Marty in particular.[6] He was to repeat it many times until success was obtained.

Frédéric Joliot followed these events attentively and later summarized his impressions of that time:[7]

I admired Langevin's lectures which we attended and I knew something about his social work and his left-wing ideas. This was the time when the trial of the Black Sea sailors was giving rise to passionate debates. "Has an officer the right to rebel?" That was the question often asked, and most people

---

[6] Units of the French navy had been sent to Odessa in order to try and overthrow the Soviet regime. Mutinies broke out among the crews in 1917 and again in 1919. In 1919 Marty, who had taken an active part, was reduced to the ranks and sentenced to twenty years' forced labor. The pressure of French public opinion secured a pardon for him.

[7] Rouzé, *op. cit.,* p. 27.

in our circles condemned André Marty. I supported him, following Langevin's example. I admired Langevin for his campaign on behalf of André Marty and André Marty for the course he had chosen.

After his time at the École de Physique et de Chimie, Frédéric Joliot spent six months (from May 10 to November 10, 1924) at Poitiers doing full-time training as an officer cadet of the artillery reserve. He finished up as a second lieutenant with a good class mark, but he was something of a disappointment to the lieutenant instructor who had hoped to find in him the star pupil not only of his brigade, the fortieth, but of the whole school. Actually up until Christmas, 1923, Frédéric Joliot had been brilliantly successful in this new cycle of studies; then suddenly he stopped taking much interest. He readily explained this as a reaction against the atmosphere of the school where he felt that beyond the purely technical training it was a question of imposing on his mind conditioned reflexes, against which his independent spirit rebelled.

At the beginning of 1925 demobilization was near at hand. He was soon to leave the service of the anti-gas corps at Aubervilliers, and it was time to find his first job.

One of the favorite memories which Frédéric Joliot liked to recount to his friends was the story of the visit he made with me to Paul Langevin's flat on the mezzanine floor of number 10 bis, Boulevard de Port-Royal. We were both of us still in doubt about which direction to take at the end of our military service, and Frédéric Joliot was still full of the enthusiasm aroused by his training period from August 21 to September 30, 1922 at the Arbed steel works at Esch-sur-Alzette (Luxembourg). Industry attracted him, with its technical questions and human problems, but his period at the École and his reading had also given him a love of research and a veneration for the great scientists. So when we learned of the possibility of benefitting from "Rothschild scholarships" to do research, our decision was quickly made.

However Paul Langevin regarded it as important to warn us. He explained that the salaries granted to teachers and researchers were markedly inferior to those normally paid in industry. Furthermore the fact of not having been to the École Normale Supérieure or the École Polytechnique consti-tuted a very serious handicap in view of the traditions and influences within the scientific profession. "You will find it very difficult to rise. That is," he added, "unless you do quite exceptional work."

A few days later he informed us that Madame Curie was willing to take on Joliot and he himself was willing to take me on as an assistant.

Scientific culture, an introduction to social problems, his first job . . . Joliot was thinking of all that when he said at Paul Langevin's funeral on December 21, 1946: "If I wanted to describe those circumstances in which I felt my life to have been closely dependent on your affectionate influence, I should have to tell the whole story, for it is to you that I owe my basic culture and knowledge."

Thus at the age of twenty-five Joliot, the young engineer, presented himself before Madame Curie one day in 1925.

I can see her now at her desk, small, with gray hair and very bright eyes. I sat before her in an officer's uniform (at that time I was doing my military service in the anti-gas corps) and I was very nervous. She listened to what I had to say and then asked me briskly: "Can you begin work tomorrow?"

I had three weeks of my service to complete. She resolved: "I will write to your colonel." The next day I became her personal assistant.[8]

It was not all that easy for him to adapt himself. There had been little taught about radioactivity at the École and he had to start all over again from the beginning. Not only did he have to be initiated into this science, he also had to take more examinations, first the "Baccalauréat" (final examination) of which he had never bothered to take the second part, then those for his *licencié* certificates (master's degree). But these hurdles were not too difficult. More tricky were the problems resulting from a change of environment.

At home and at the Lycée Lakanal his environment had been that of the comfortable middle classes. Thanks to his sister Marguerite, a talented painter, he had frequented artists' studios, and his taste for painting no doubt originated from these visits. At the École Lavoisier and at the École de Physique et de Chimie his friends had come more from working-class than from middle-class homes, and he had been struck by the stronger element of competition and by the way they took their work more seriously. Now he was to enter the academic world.

A stone's throw from the Panthéon there is a relatively new street which runs between the Rue d'Ulm and the Rue

[8] Interview with F. Joliot-Curie (*Gazette de Lausanne*, June 29, 1957).

Saint-Jacques. It has been named the Rue Pierre Curie. At number 11 in this street stands the Radium Institute—the laboratory which the great scientist dreamed of all his life and which he never obtained. (It is significant that one of the chapters in Marie Curie's book on Pierre Curie's life is called "The Struggle for Equipment." From the little shady garden behind the main building one can see, on a raised level several feet up, the bay windows of Marie Curie's study. Everything has been left as it was after her daughter and then Frédéric Joliot occupied it successively.

It is in this building that Frédéric Joliot began his career as a physicist and met Irène.

It was not easy for a very young man to confront Madame Curie, surrounded with glory as she was, and made even more unapproachable by her own shyness. Moreover, Paul Langevin's warnings proved to have been justified. Not being from the École Normale Supérieure, the young engineer from the École de Physique et de Chimie was to some extent regarded as an outsider, and it took many years of first-class work before all traces of ostracism had disappeared—even after his marriage to Irène Curie.

Irène's position in the laboratory was a special one: she was both the daughter and the assistant of "la Patronne." She had a great knowledge of radioactivity. Her imperturbable calm and her direct manner in replying to questions quite misleadingly made her seem cold and somewhat haughty.

At first Frédéric Joliot had the same impression of her as other people did. Through his work as an assistant and his quickly recognized ability, he was soon working with her more and more often and was shortly able to discern the reality beneath the surface appearance. Many years later, in conversation with one of his biographers, he described in the following words the way his feelings developed:

At that time I had not the slightest idea that we might one day marry. But I observed her. It began with my observing her. Presenting a cold exterior—she sometimes forgot to say "Good morning"—she did not always create a feeling of sympathy around her at the lab. But as I observed her, I discovered in this girl, whom other people regarded somewhat as a block of ice, an extraordinary person, sensitive and poetic, who in many things gave the impression of being a living replica of what her father had been. I had read much about Pierre Curie, I had heard teachers who had known him

talking about him and I rediscovered in his daughter the same
purity, the same good sense and humility. . . .

Irène Curie was three years older than Frédéric Joliot, and
seemed at first to be his opposite in everything. She was as
calm and serene as he was impulsive. By nature very reserved, she found it difficult to make friends, while he was
able to make human contact with everyone. She took little
interest in her appearance and dress, while he was good-
looking, elegant, and always a great success with the
opposite sex. In argument Irène was incapable of the least
deceit or artifice or of making the smallest concession. With
an implacable obstinacy she would present her thesis, meeting her interlocutor head on, even if he occupied a very
high social position. Frédéric Joliot, on the other hand, without
conceding a point, had a wonderful ability to use his
psychological understanding to put his opponents in a frame
of mind in which they could accept his arguments.

Anyone who met Irène surrounded by her apparatus and
believed—as many people did—that she could only live in
the laboratory and for the laboratory, was greatly mistaken.
From her childhood she had been devoted to sports and
she excelled chiefly at swimming and skiing. She was intensely fond of nature and in particular of the mountain
country, where on several occasions she had had to stay on
account of lung infections.

Irène had inherited her father's noble brow and her mother's
bright and limpid eyes. Her whole person radiated frankness
and kindness. Her exterior, which tended to be cold, con-
cealed a passionate nature. She had a profound knowledge
of French, English and German poetry and her preference
fluctuated between Béranger, Heine, and Kipling.

It was in the course of long walks through the forest
of Fontainebleau that the "daughter-assistant" and the "en-
gineer-assistant" talked of physics, art, and religion and realized that they were in love with one another.

We understood that it would be difficult for us to do without one another. We had differing but complementary temper-
aments. The best partnerships for work, as for life, are not
those made up of like characters but those made up of complementary ones.[9]

[9] Rouzé, *op. cit.*, p. 32.

3

The Man and Science

THE FIRST STEPS

As SOON as he was installed at the Radium Institute, Frédéric Joliot plunged with enthusiasm into his work. At first his drive and impetuosity—as he discovered only later—caused Madame Curie and her daughter some anxiety.

While continuing until 1927 to work for the examinations for his *licencié ès sciences* degree, he began by familiarizing himself with the experimental techniques of the laboratory. At the same time, in order to supplement his low salary, he arranged, also in 1927, to give the course of lectures in electrical measurements at the École d'Electricité Industrielle Charliot. He took this on not without apprehension, as he later recalled: "For the first time I was going to find myself in front of a great many pupils. After a little while this anxiety disappeared as a current of sympathy was established between the teacher and his pupils."

Finally, as an engineer, a holder of the *licencié,* and a teacher, Joliot launched out into the great adventure of scientific research.

For his first research project he studied the electrolysis of dilute solutions of salts of radioactive elements. The latter were deposited onto an electrode which consisted of a thin sheet of mica covered by a very fine film of gold. On the other side of the mica sheet was an ionization chamber which made it possible to observe the radiation emitted, from which could be deduced the speed at which the radioactive elements were deposited.

In 1927 the name of Frédéric Joliot appeared for the first time in the *Comptes Rendus* (reports) of the Académie des Sciences.*

The young scientist's curiosity was then naturally directed

* See the Bibliography, p. 187, for a listing of some of his many scientific articles.

toward this layer of gold which was sufficient to constitute an electrode, while at the same time permitting the passage of the alpha rays from polonium. He therefore undertook a systematic study of the conditions of preparation and the physical properties of these fine layers of metal. He even succeeded in depositing the metal on a support which he then dissolved in acetone, thus producing a true metal plate, without a support, a few hundred thousandths of a millimeter thick. This process was later used by the British physicist G. P. Thomson in studying the diffraction of electrons. Joliot did not stake further claims in this direction, but it is only right to recognize that he had perform true piece of pioneering work in a field which today has seen great scientific and industrial development.

Joliot resumed his researches in radioactivity, and in 1928, for the first time a note appeared in the *Comptes Rendus* of the Académie des Sciences bearing the two names of Frédéric Joliot and Irène Curie.[2]

In 1930 Joliot submitted his doctoral thesis on "The Study of the Electrochemistry of Radioactive Elements."

It was about that time that one of his old friends made the following remark to him, half in earnest and half joking: "You've come too late to study radioactivity. The radioactive decay series of these substances are known and there is hardly anything left to do other than evaluate to the third or fourth decimal place the various quantities which characterize them."

Events did not confirm this pessimistic attitude. In any case there was no risk of its discouraging the young researcher.

In many countries the attention of physicists was being directed toward the phenomena caused by the passage of alpha rays through matter. Some of these phenomena occur only very rarely: hence the interest in having a source which gave off a large number of these alpha rays. Polonium[3] is particularly useful for this type of work. The sources existing in the laboratory of the Radium Institute at that time were of insufficient intensity, but within the gram and a half of

[2] Irène Curie had married Joliot in 1926 but as she had already published many scientific works under her maiden name, she continued under the name of Madame Irène Curie.

[3] A radioactive element discovered in 1898 by Pierre and Marie Curie in pitchblende. It was given this name in honor of Madame Curie's native country.

radium which Madame Curie had at her disposal, a great deal of polonium had accumulated: this the two young scientists undertook to isolate.

It was a delicate and dangerous task because of the great amount of radioactivity present. This is how Frédéric Joliot described these operations in the account he wrote about his scientific work:

The manipulation of this dangerous substance in such concentrations is a delicate matter and calls for numerous precautions, in view of the danger from the intense radiations which are given off. These extractions made it possible to quadruple the amount of RaD available in the laboratory. In collaboration with Madame Joliot-Curie I perfected the techniques used to prepare sources of polonium of very great activity: either by electrolysis or by evaporation.

The considerable effort required for the preparation of a source of 200 millicuries was soon to be rewarded.

RESEARCH ON THE NEUTRON

It was now 1932. Little Hélène Joliot was five. At the beginning of the year Irène Joliot-Curie took part enthusiastically in the experiments they had decided on together although she was due to give birth, in March, to her son Pierre.

Two years previously the German scientists Bothe and Becker had observed something very curious: While bombarding light elements such as boron and beryllium with alpha rays, they observed that a radiation was emitted, a radiation so penetrating that after passing through ten centimeters of lead its intensity was hardly reduced. All nuclear physicists were greatly perplexed. Could this be a radiation of the same type as the gamma rays emitted by radium? That was the opinion of the two German physicists. Under what conditions was this radiation emitted? Were they witnessing a primary effect or the final phase of a series of intermediate reactions between atomic nuclei? Frédéric and Irène Joliot had at their disposal the powerful source of alpha radiation which prolonged efforts had enabled them to produce, and they set out to repeat the experiments of the two German physicists.

The study of this unknown radiation can be undertaken in two ways, either by measurement of its intensity or by photography. These two methods both played such an important part in the Joliots' experiments that it is useful to set down briefly the principles of each.

Two parallel plates, between which a large potential difference is established, are mounted in a gas-filled container. Under these conditions only a very small electric current is detected. However, if radiation from a radioactive substance passes between the plates it ionizes the atoms present, making them electrically charged. The electric field between the plates attracts the charged atoms to the plates. The current between the plates is thus increased in proportion to the intensity of the radiation. This apparatus is called an ionization chamber.

The apparatus enabling one to see and to photograph radiation is called a cloud chamber. It was invented and constructed by the Scottish physicist C. T. R. Wilson[4] in 1912.

A cylinder, closed at the top with a sheet of glass and at the bottom with a movable piston, is filled with air saturated with water vapor. If the piston is suddenly lowered the reduction in pressure cools the gas and generally a mist appears (due to the condensation of the water vapor). If, before this experiment is performed, all traces of dust are removed from the gas, the mist is not produced. Condensation can only take place around the nuclei provided by the grains of dust. Now if radiation from a radioactive substance is passed through the cloud chamber at the moment when the pressure is reduced (or if this radiation itself automatically initiates the reduction in pressure), the radiation causes ionization and the charged ions serve as nuclei for water drops so that the trajectory of the radiation will be visible as a succession of tiny drops of water.

Joliot had constructed a cloud chamber which worked at a low pressure and made it possible to observe tracks left by radiation 76 times the length of those seen in old chambers.

Let us imagine him one day in the thirties. Wearing his white smock, he stands before an apparatus built out of pumps and motors with the cylindrical cloud chamber mounted on a vertical axis, its top closed by a sheet of glass, above which are mounted two cameras inclined at an angle of 45° to the horizontal. He has one or more visitors with him and he is describing his cloud chamber.

There are various ways of talking about a piece of

[4] C. T. R. Wilson was awarded the Nobel Prize for physics in 1927.

scientific equipment. There are, first of all, the "instructions for use" supplied by the maker. Reading them is essential but it is generally a dry and disheartening business. Or one can give a rapid description of the general construction, followed by an explanation of the results obtained with it.

Joliot's explanation is to some extent a combination of those which a poet and an engineer would each have given from their own points of view. In a few minutes he illustrates all the avenues of research opened up by this technique invented by the famous Scottish physicist. With the good workman's affection for the thing he has made, he explains the modifications he has contributed and shows the parts he designed himself or altered in the workshop. His hand lingers in passing over a nut, a window, or a piston, and he relives, at that moment, the various stages of the conception and the construction and also the moment when the first results were obtained. His gestures are as expressive as his words. One could really say that he models his thought with his hands.

"In this chamber an infinitely tiny particle reveals its own trajectory, in a succession of drops of condensation. Is it not the most beautiful phenomenon in the world?" he asks with the air of a connoisseur.

And if Irène has joined the group she will certainly reply: "Yes, my dear, it would be the most beautiful phenomenon in the world, if there were not that of childbirth."

Joliot's deep interest in the cloud chamber so impressed all his colleagues that one of them, H. Halban, recalled it in a lecture given to the Société Française de Physique.[5]

The cloud chamber remained Joliot's favorite instrument. He always had several of them in perfect working order available. He spent long hours making visual observations by means of these instruments. These periods constituted a kind of retreat which was essential to him. But from time to time one of his colleagues had the privilege of spending an afternoon alone in the dim room with him, watching. During these hours he gave free rein to his imagination, and these interviews were a source of great inspiration to many of us.

At the end of 1931 Frédéric and Irène Joliot-Curie had at their disposal the powerful source of alpha rays, the preparation of which had involved so much long and detailed work. In order to study the properties and the effect on

[5] *Journal de Physique*, October, 1959, pp. 40 ff.

matter of the mysterious radiation discovered by Bothe and Becker, they decided first of all to use the ionization chamber.

In order to be quite sure of having only the very penetrating radiation, they first passed the radiation through fifteen millimeters of lead before it entered the ionization chamber. On the face of it the selection of the shielding material for the chamber did not seem to pose any difficult problems since several extra centimeters of lead would still not present a significant obstacle. However, the two physicists decided to seal the ionization chamber with no more than a very thin layer of aluminum—only five thousandths of a millimeter thick. Under these conditions if the unknown radiation, in passing through different substances, produced an easily absorbed radiation, the latter also could enter the ionization chamber and be detected. It was this decision, which allowed the maximum possibilities for observation, which lay at the heart of the discovery. Joliot drew the same moral himself in a paper he wrote in 1954.

I always attached great importance to the way an experiment is set up and performed. It is certainly necessary to begin with a preconceived idea, but whenever possible the experiment should be devised in such a way as to open as many windows as possible on the unexpected. The more one achieves without difficulty the less one achieves in fact.

Thus they made their first measurements using an ionization chamber. Then they interposed various sheets of absorber in the beam of radiation entering the chamber. The current through the chamber should have diminished. In fact it either remained constant or else it *increased* (in the case of cellophane and paraffin). This was interpreted as the production of something else. And this "something else" could not have entered the ionization chamber if the wall had been even a few tenths of a millimeter thicker. The presence of a thicker wall would have masked the phenomenon.

At once Frédéric and Irène Joliot-Curie decided to use the cloud chamber to enable them to see, to photograph, and to identify this radiation. By this means they were able to establish that "Bothe and Becker's radiation" was capable of colliding with and projecting forward nuclei of hydrogen, helium, or nitrogen. They also observed that high-energy electrons were simultaneously ejected from the sheet. When they published the results of these elegant experiments, they accompanied them with a tentative interpretation, even though they themselves had reservations about the correctness of their hypotheses.

The results were published on January 18, 1932. A month later on February 17 at the Cavendish Laboratory, Cambridge, on the other side of the Channel, the British physicist James Chadwick gave the correct interpretation of these various observations. He had available a piece of electronic equipment—the linear amplifier—which was still lacking in Paris. With this he was able to measure individually the impulses produced by the projected nuclei and to separate them from those caused by the electrons. He demonstrated that none of the hypotheses so far advanced was acceptable, but that everything could be explained if one postulated that the "Bothe and Becker radiation" consisted of *electrically neutral* particles which had approximately the mass of the hydrogen nucleus. Chadwick christened these particles "neutrons."

The role of this elementary particle has become so important and its name is so familiar today that it is difficult to appreciate the genius of observation, imagination, and deduction needed to establish its existence. (Who is astonished today to discover that the earth is round and revolves around the sun?)

The history of this important discovery constitutes a fine example of international cooperation between scientists:

1930: Bothe and Becker (Germany)
1932: Frédéric and Irène Joliot-Curie (France)
1932: J. Chadwick (Great Britain).

It is relatively easy, once the decisive step has been taken toward a new discovery, to trace how it came about and its significance. It is much harder to imagine the hesitations, the leaps forward, the enthusiasms, and the disappointments of the period which precedes success.

The following extracts from letters written by Frédéric Joliot to his friend in Moscow, D. Skobeltsin, give some idea of this:

At the same time (work in the workshop being rather slow) Madame Joliot and I have been busy with experiments concerning the phenomenon discovered by Bothe and Becker of the production of penetrating gamma rays issuing from light nuclei when they are bombarded with alpha particles. We have discovered new and interesting results.

From Marie Curie's house at Arcouest in Brittany he wrote again on April 2, 1932:

I am taking advantage of a brief holiday in Brittany to write to you. First of all I must announce that we have a son, born on March 12. Madame Joliot is in good health and is still resting in Paris. We have been working hard during the last few months and I was very tired before I left for Brittany. We had to speed up the pace of our experiments, for it is annoying to be overtaken by other laboratories which immediately take up one's experiments. In Paris this was done straight away by Monsieur Maurice de Broglie with Thibaut and two other colleagues. In Cambridge Chadwick did not wait long to do so either. He has, by the way, published the very attractive hypothesis that the penetrating radiation from $Po(\alpha)Be$ is composed of neutrons. I tell you this because I believe you are in touch via *C.R.*[6] and *Nature*[7] with these experiments, concerning the projection of atomic nuclei.

We have recently been carrying out new experiments on the $Po(\alpha)Be$ radiation and the results will be published on Monday in the *C.R.* Here is a summary. $Po(\alpha)Be$ radiation is composed of at least two parts: one part is gamma rays of energy between 5 and 11 MeV and is scattered by the Compton effect. The other part is radiation of *enormous*[8] penetrating power— about half is absorbed in 16 cm. of Pb following collisions with the nuclei. This radiation is very probably composed of neutrons.[9]

THE DISCOVERY OF ARTIFICIAL RADIOACTIVITY

It has always been an oddity of scientific history that the discovery of artificial radioactivity was not made many years before 1933. It certainly could have been if a determined search for it had been made with the normally available strong radioactive sources and sensitive electrometers.

In fact the Joliot-Curies' discovery of induced radioactivity arose out of two independent discoveries, that of the neutron and of the positron. That is what P. M. S. Blackett[10] states in the account of Joliot's life which he wrote for the Royal Society of London.

We have already examined the role played by Frédéric

[6] The *Comptes Rendus* of the Académie des Sciences.

[7] The British scientific weekly, much appreciated because of the speed with which letters to the editor are published.

[8] Underlined in the letter.

[9] We are particularly grateful to Professor D. Skobeltsin for kindly sending us photocopies of the letters, almost all written by hand, which Frédéric Joliot-Curie wrote to him.

[10] "Jean-Frédéric Joliot," *Biographical Memoirs of Fellows of the Royal Society*, VI (1960), 87–101.

and Irène Joliot-Curie in the first of these discoveries, that of the neutron. The second of the discoveries, that of the positron, or positive electron, was made in 1932 by the American physicist C. Anderson. Blackett and Occhialini, in Britain, opened up this line of research, while the Joliot-Curies in France took the first photograph, in a cloud chamber, of the simultaneous production of a positive electron and a negative electron.

It was then that the two French scientists embarked upon the research which was to class them firmly among the great discoverers.

I will never forget that afternnon in the middle of January, 1934, when a telephone call made me leave my laboratory in the Rue Vauquelin and hurry to the Radium Institute in the Rue Pierre Curie, where Frédéric Joliot was waiting for me in a semi-basement room.

The apparatus which he wanted to show me consisted of equipment scattered over several tables. Its newness and apparent disorder revealed to even the least alert observer that here was an experiment set up in haste, to reproduce as a demonstration a discovery made several hours beforehand with Irène. Later on, the setting up of the demonstration would be more neat and studied, less spontaneous.

Joliot summarized for me the experiments previously carried out in this field, taking great care—as he always did—to specify the part played by each of them. Then he came to his own experiment: "I irradiate this target with alpha rays from my source: you can hear the Geiger counter crackling. I remove the source: the crackling ought to stop, but in fact it continues. . . ."

At that moment the laboratory door opened behind the experimenter, who was once more overcome with enthusiasm for his discovery, and Marie Curie and Paul Langevin came in.

The demonstration was performed again with the same precision and simplicity.

The scene I have just described lasted hardly more than half an hour. Few words were exchanged, apart from several brief questions and the precise replies they received. I was not the only person to have retained an unforgettable memory of it. Joliot often later reminded me of that moment and spoke of his emotion, his pride and his joy at having been able to offer before these two scientists, to whom he was bound by so many ties, a fresh example of the vital character and ever-widening horizons of science.

Some time after that there was another historic moment for Frédéric and Irène Joliot-Curie: the moment when they presented to Marie Curie the first *chemically isolated* artificially radioactive element. In a talk he was to have given on Radiodiffusion-Télévision Française in 1957, but which was banned by the government of the time and published in the magazine *La Nef,* Frédéric Joliot-Curie spoke of that moment in these words:

Marie Curie saw our research work and I will never forget the expression of intense joy which came over her when Irène and I showed her the first artificially radioactive element in a little glass tube. I can still see her taking in her fingers (which were already burnt with radium) this little tube containing the radioactive compound—as yet one in which the activity was very weak. To verify what we had told her she held it near a Geiger-Müller counter and she could hear the rate meter giving off a great many "clicks." This was doubtless the last great satisfaction of her life. A few months later Marie Curie died of leukemia.

The consequences of the discovery of artificial radioactivity have become so familiar that its place in the general perspective of the progress of science is often not properly appreciated. It seems useful to recapitulate this development here, even though it will be necessary to summarize a great deal.

At the end of the nineteenth century the physical and chemical properties of most of the known elements had been studied. The Russian scientist Mendeleev had put forward the brilliant idea of classifying these elements into groups according to his Periodic Table. The properties of each of these elements were quite specific and remained invariable. In whatever compound one found iron or calcium it was always the same iron and the same calcium. Despite the innumerable attempts of the alchemists, every element obstinately clung to its identity and its distinctive characteristics.

From 1898 onward the situation was changed. Thanks to the work of Henri Becquerel and Pierre and Marie Curie, assisted by Gustave Bémont, new elements were discovered in the earth's crust: radioactive elements. These substances, of which the most famous—until the discovery of fission— was radium, disintegrate spontaneously, emitting radiation and becoming, some quickly and some very slowly, different chemical elements: thus it is that radium finally becomes lead. Man observed these disintegrations and measured the rate of disintegration. He used them but he could in no way modify either their end product or their rate. Man was the fascinated spectator of a process he had not started and which he could neither speed up, slow down, nor stop. The physicist and the chemist were helpless: the dream of the alchemist remained a dream. . . .

But this dream was to be realized. In 1919—the precise year in which the young schoolboy, Frédéric Joliot entered the École de Physique et de Chimie as a pupil—the great physicist Ernest Rutherford succeeded in *observing* a transmutation in a non-naturally radioactive material. This fundamental experiment, which must be counted among those which have modified the whole course of physics as well as the destiny of mankind, was recalled in the following words by Irène Joliot-Curie in her Nobel Prize lecture on December 12, 1935:

Following the discovery of the spontaneous transmutations of radioactive elements it is to Lord Rutherford that we owe the realization of the first artificial transmutations. Some fifteen years after the initial discovery of radioactivity, Lord Rutherford demonstrated the ejection of *protons* (positively charged hydrogen nuclei) from light elements, such as nitrogen or aluminum, when bombarded with alpha rays. These hydrogen nuclei came from the bombarded atoms themselves: they were the results of transmutations. It has been possible to establish with certainty the nature of this nuclear reaction: for example, the aluminum nucleus captures an alpha particle and, after expelling a proton, transmutes itself into an atom of silicon. The quantity of matter transformed is much too small to be weighed and it is only the study of the radiations which has led to these conclusions.

As always, this pioneer work gave a new impulse to research. Numerous atomic nuclei were bombarded by the various projectiles which were featured at that time in the arsenals of the nuclear physicists. It was necessary now to add to the already known "chemical reactions" of an element the "nuclear reactions" of the atom's nucleus. In the case of the first it is the atoms which combine themselves in various ways to form the innumerable molecules of inorganic and organic chemistry. In the case of the second it is the chemical nature of the bombarded nucleus of the atom itself which is changed.

The study of these nuclear reactions immediately posed delicate and complex problems. For every reaction the balance sheet of masses and energies had to be drawn up. The chemical change had to be identified and related to the nature of the radiation emitted.

The history of science is rich in these periods of rapid expansion. A new phenomenon has just been discovered and a theoretical interpretation seems as if it ought to account for it correctly. On this basis researchers in every country carry out new experiments. They have some success but difficulties remain. Certain observed facts obstinately refuse to fit in with the new theory. It is in such cases that one can most easily recognize the stroke of genius of the scientist who in a confused situation succeeds in drawing the meaningful conclusion, or in performing the experiment which tears aside the veil. No example is more characteristic in this respect than the discovery of artificial radioactivity.

In order to put it in perspective and understand it properly let us go back to the "Conseil Solvay" held in Brussels in October, 1933.

The meetings arranged annually by the Solvay foundation are among the most important of those which scientists from different countries periodically attend to exchange the results of their experiments as well as their theoretical ideas on subjects of current interest. That year there were gathered about Paul Langevin, who presided, the greatest physicists of the twentieth century: Marie Curie, Lord Rutherford, P. A. M. Dirac, P. M. S. Blackett, Niels Bohr, P. Debye, Enrico Fermi, Louis de Broglie, A. Yoffé, W. Pauli, and many others.

Irène Joliot-Curie and Frédéric Joliot presented a report entitled: "Penetrating Radiation from Atoms Bombarded by Alpha Rays." By bombarding various substances with alpha rays they had been able to observe the emission of protons. But in the case of light elements, such as aluminum, they found that they were observing the simultaneous emission of a neutron and a positive electron.

Their account aroused extremely animated discussions. The German physicist, Lise Meitner, reported that she had carried out the same experiment as the two French physicists and had never observed anything other than the re-emission of a proton.

Could there have been an error in their conduct of the experiment? Was the interpretation they gave of their results incorrect? Though Frédéric and Irène Joliot-Curie were very certain of the results of their work, they were nevertheless shaken by the reception they were given. Fortunately two of the scientists present, and not the least of them, sensed that they were faced with something fundamental. As Joliot wrote later:

The great majority of the physicists there did not believe our experiments had been accurate. After the meeting we were feeling rather depressed. But at that moment Professor Niels Bohr took my wife and me to one side and told us he thought our results were very important. A little later Pauli gave us similar encouragement.

Back in Paris they started work again. The debates at the Solvay Conference induced them to carry out basic experiments devised to verify the theories of Dirac, while continuing to follow their previous procedure. At the Radium Institute and at home—insofar as little Hélène, who was now several years old, left them the leisure to do so—during and after meals, they continued to discuss their results and returned to the laboratory each day with a well-prepared plan of procedure.

And so it continued through the weeks. . . . For, contrary to popular belief, scientific discoveries are not the happy chance result of a few experiments. As Marie Curie[11] wrote:

A great discovery does not issue from the scientist's brain ready-made, like Minerva springing fully armed from Jupiter's head; it is the fruit of an accumulation of preliminary work. Between the days which are fruitful and productive come days of uncertainty, when nothing seems to go right, when matter itself seems hostile, and it is then that one must fight against discouragement.

It was in the course of the "hostile days" that Frédéric Joliot made the best use of his genius and forced success to come. He never yielded to discouragement. Not in the laboratory, nor when he became the victim of injustices, nor when he lost Irène. He could always find, in his confidence in man and in his love and understanding of nature, the means to resist it.

Thus, after the Solvay Conference at Brussels the idea for the experiment which would succeed in removing all their doubts came to them little by little. As soon as the procedure for it had been agreed on with Irène, Joliot set about carrying it out with the speed and elegance that always characterized his work.

[11] *Pierre Curie* by Marie Curie, Denoel, 1955, p. 95.

Did the emission of neutrons and the associated positive electrons depend on the speed of the projectile used to bombard the nucleus? And, above all, was it possible, as in the case of Rutherford's experiments, that there was an instantaneous nuclear reaction? . . . But let us allow Joliot himself to describe the experiment he carried out:

We were surprised to observe that as one progressively reduces the energy of the alpha rays, the emission of neutrons ceases altogether when a minimum velocity is reached, while that of positive electrons continues and decreases only over a period of time, like the radiation of electrons from a naturally radioactive element. We repeated the experiment in a simplified form. We bombarded aluminum with alpha rays with their maximum velocity. Then, after a certain period of irradiation, we removed the source of alpha rays. We now observed that the sheet of aluminum continued to emit positive electrons over a period of several minutes. Everything became clear!

Everything became clear—provided they were certain that the crackling of the Geiger counter was indeed caused by an unexpected radiation and not by a fault in the mechanism.

It was six o'clock in the evening when Joliot asked himself this question. He and his wife had accepted an invitation for that evening and could not put it off. Fortunately, a specialist in Geiger counters, the young German physicist W. Gentner, had been working in the laboratory since January, 1933. Joliot called him and explained the problem to him. He described the crackling and asked him to be so kind as to check to see if the counters were in good working order.

That evening Frédéric and Irène's hosts must have found them distracted and thoughtful at times. At all events the following morning the Joliots found on their desk a little hand-written note from Gentner, telling them that the Geiger counters were in perfect working order. It was not a defeat. It was a new phenomenon.

To the physicist all was now clear. There could be no doubt about the existence of the new radioactive element. But to the chemist? For the chemist an element exists beyond doubt only if one can isolate it and show it in a test tube. In this particular case only infinitesimal quantities of the new element had been formed. Furthermore this element disintegrated spontaneously—often very quickly—leaving the chemist only a few minutes to analyze it in its radioactive form. When they bombarded aluminum, half the newly formed radioactive material, radiophosphorus, disappeared within three minutes, fifteen seconds. Within three minutes Joliot had identified it chemically. The demonstration was complete.

On January 15, 1934, an account published in the *Comptes Rendus* of the Académie des Sciences to some extent constituted the official birth certificate of artificial radioactivity. This account may be considered as a model of its kind (the text is given on page 153).

Two weeks later, on February 1, 1934, Joliot wrote a letter to his friend and colleague, D. Skobeltsin. The latter has drawn attention in an article[12] to the reserved tone, which emphasizes "not only the modesty of the writer, but also his desire, resulting from this modesty, not to overemphasize the value of the result he had obtained."

Here is the characteristic passage from this letter: the original contains the abbreviations commonly used in correspondence between colleagues and friends:

We were not mistaken about the positive electrons from transmutations, for we have recently discovered the following fact: the emission of positrons from sheets of B or Al or Mg irradiated with α from Po continues to take place even when one removes the Po source. This goes on for quite a long time. One actually produces true radioactive material, with half-lives of 14′ for B, 3′15″ Al, 2′30″ Mg. We have *isolated* and identified chemically the nuclei formed in the case of irradiated B and Al—they are N and P.

There is a prospect of plenty of work ahead, for one should be able to produce these isotopes or others by bombarding matter with other particles, e.g. the proton or deuteron.

Today there are not only two or three artificially radioactive elements which can be produced by man, but approximately a thousand, which have mean lives ranging from minute fractions of a second to thousands of years. As for the consequences of the discovery, they are of great importance, both for our basic knowledge and for their application in industry, medicine, and many other fields.

The Joliots' discovery did no more than reveal the possibility of creating artificially radioactive elements. Until then it had been well known that the decomposition of naturally radioactive elements was accompanied by the emission of three types of radiation:

[12] *La Pensée,* No. 87 (1959), p. 45.

alpha rays (α) (nuclei of helium)
beta rays ($\beta-$) (negative electrons)
gamma rays (γ) (electromagnetic waves)
They had now established that another type of radiation can also be emitted in the course of the decomposition of artificial radio-elements:
positive beta rays ($\beta+$) or positrons
As we have shown, the physicists Anderson, Blackett, and Occhialini had already observed the production of this new elementary particle through the action of cosmic rays.

The Joliots received a great number of letters at that time. On January 30, 1934, one letter particularly caught their attention. It came from Cambridge and bore the signature of the great physicist Ernest Rutherford. For many years he had dreamed of phenomena of the kind which they had discovered. He at once wrote the following letter to his young French colleagues:

My dear Colleagues

I was delighted to see an account of your experiments in producing a radioactive body by exposure to α rays. I congratulate you both on a fine piece of work which I am sure will ultimately prove of much importance.

I am personally very much interested in your results as I have long thought that some such an effect should be observed under the right conditions. In the past I have tried a number of such experiments using a sensitive electroscope to detect such effects but without any success. We also tried the effect of protons last year on the heavy elements but with negative results.

With best wishes to you both for the further success of your investigations.

                                        Rutherford

We shall try and see whether similar effects appear in proton or diplon[13] bombardment.

Few tributes were as simple, as sincere and as much appreciated.

NUCLEAR FISSION

The discovery of artificial radioactivity and the award of the Nobel Prize brought Frédéric Joliot into the public eye. France—it must be admitted—did not discover him until after the other countries.

In 1934 he was elected Maître de Conférences at the

[13] "Diplon" was the name at that time proposed by Rutherford for the deuteron.

Sorbonne. Three years later the Collège de France opened its doors to him.

In addition to his responsibilities as a teacher there, he had the delicate and absorbing task of directing numerous French and foreign research workers, among them Halban, Kowarski, Pontecorvo, and Savel. But now Joliot was to delight in turning to an activity which depended more on his qualities as an engineer than on those of the physicist.

In order to extend the field of experiment, and have any hope of new results, Marie Curie had always emphasized the extreme importance of preparing powerful sources of radioactivity. She had prepared them herself. Irène and Frédéric had followed her example, with the success we have seen.

Since 1930, then, the atomic physicist's artillery had been augmented by a new weapon, the cyclotron, invented by the American physicist E. O. Lawrence. These machines were now to permit nuclear physicists to pursue and extend their investigations by providing them with sources of radioactivity several hundred times more powerful than natural sources. Joliot did not want his own country to lag behind the others in this and undertook to provide equipment for France. At the École des Travaux Publics at Arcueil-Cachan he constructed with M. Feldenkrais and A. Lazard an accelerator of the Van de Graaf type which provided a potential of a million volts. The two columns of this machine —each surmounted with a metal sphere large enough to accommodate a laboratory and its experimenters—greeted the visitors to the Palace of Discovery at the Universal Exhibition in 1937.

At Ivry he had the "Ampère Laboratory" of the Companie Générale Electrocéramique transformed and equipped. Helped by A. Lazard and P. Saval he installed an impulse generator there which could provide three million volts. This laboratory was acquired by the Centre National de la Recherche Scientifique (C.N.R.S.) and was named the "Atomic Synthesis Laboratory." Joliot was to direct it until the end of his life and later had new buildings added to it which were set aside for chemical and biological research.

Finally at the Collège de France he had a cyclotron built. The energy transmitted to the accelerated particles was equivalent to 7 million electron volts, which seems very modest today if one thinks of the machines a thousand times more powerful which exist at Geneva, Dubna

(U.S.S.R.), Harwell (England), or Brookhaven (U.S.A.). But it was the first cyclotron in Europe outside the U.S.S.R.

During this period Irène Joliot-Curie, along with her other activities, devoted a considerable part of her time to research on "transuranic" elements. Events were soon to bring Joliot back to his calling as a physicist.

In 1935 new research was undertaken in many countries which was to lead to discoveries with immense repercussions. Using the recently discovered neutrons as projectiles, Enrico Fermi had bombarded the heaviest and most complex atom of all those known at that time—uranium. He observed that new bodies were formed which had radioactive properties. Fermi presumed that the neutron had become attached to the uranium nucleus. A new, *heavier,* nucleus would thus be created: this he called the "transuranium."

These studies were taken up by Lise Meitner (first in Berlin and then in Sweden, where she fled because of racial persecution), by Otto Hahn and Fritz Strassmann in Germany, and by Irène Joliot-Curie and the Yugoslav physicist P. Savitch in Paris. In 1938 these two announced a quite unexpected result which at first was met by incredulity on the part of the specialists: In the course of the nuclear reactions initiated by the bombardment of uranium nuclei by neutrons, nuclei were formed with chemical properties which resembled those of "rare earths." These bodies were not heavier than uranium: they were lighter. Did "transuranium" exist?

Some time after the publication of the results obtained by Irène Joliot-Curie and P. Savitch, Joliot went to Rome to take part in an international congress of chemists. He met there the German scientist Otto Hahn who has recently described their encounter in these words: "We had known one another's work on radium for a long time without ever having met in person. We quickly established a personal and friendly contact."

In the course of the discussion about the surprising results of the experiments carried out by Irène Joliot-Curie and P. Savitch, Hahn was moved to speak to Joliot more or less as follows: "I have great friendship and admiration for your wife. Nevertheless I have decided to repeat her experiments and I think I shall soon be able to show that she has made a mistake."

Hahn was as good as his word. Assisted by Fritz Strassmann he repeated the experiments, extending them, and in

December, 1938, these two scientists were able to confirm definitely that uranium irradiated by neutrons gave rise to much lighter elements. With extreme hesitation they suggested that it was possible to consider that the uranium nucleus had been split into two under the action of the neutrons.

The article published by Hahn and Strassmann arrived at the Joliots' laboratory on January 16, 1939. Quite understandably it caused a sensation there: the results published by Irène Joliot-Curie and Savitch were confirmed.

Joliot at once began to discuss the matter with his wife and there and then formulated the basic ideas about the mechanism of nuclear fission, notably the fact that it was possible for the number of neutrons emitted from the nuclei which had been bombarded to be greater than the number of incident neutrons. It still remained to give the direct experimental proof of nuclear fission.

Joliot first turned his attention to the neutrons which might eventually escape from a mass of uranium which had itself been bombarded with neutrons. His techniques were limited here: as at the time of his experiments on the Bothe and Becker radiation, he lacked linear amplifiers. He therefore decided to examine not the neutrons but the fission fragments. If the nucleus is split in two by the absorption of a neutron it should be possible to recover the fragments of it. But at what speed will these fragments be projected? Joliot's estimation of the balance sheet of energy for the reaction led him to caluclate the energy liberated in the course of fission to be 200 Me V.[14] The fission fragments, if they did indeed possess this amount of energy, should be able to travel a distance of about three centimeters through air.

"Very few physicists would have made that prediction correctly. It was easy for Joliot who had, in his time, made a study of the recoil of nuclei in the cloud chamber."[15]

The equipment Joliot conceived of to test this hypothesis was particularly simple and elegant: the uranium subjected to bombardment by neutrons was put on the exterior surface of a small brass cylinder, with an external diameter of twenty millimeters and a height of five centimeters (in point

[14] The "Me V" is an abbreviation for a million electron-volts. An energy of 200 Me V is thus equivalent to the energy which would be possessed by an electron accelerated in a machine which produced 200 million volts.

[15] H. Halban, *Journal de Physique*, October, 1959, pp. 38 ff. This important article deals with the whole of Joliot's scientific work.

of fact the exterior surface was covered with uranium paint). The source of neutrons (radium plus beryllium) was placed inside the cylinder. If the uranium underwent fission under the action of the neutrons, then the fragments ejected ought to be collected on a Bakelite cylinder, concentric with the first and slightly larger in diameter (internal diameter: twenty-six millimeters). Joliot first of all performed two preliminary control experiments.

a. In the absence of the cylinder covered with uranium the source of neutrons did not produce artificially radioactive material on the Bakelite cylinder.

b. If one put the cylinder covered in uranium in place, but *not the source of neutrons*, once again no radioactivity appeared on the Bakelite cylinder.

Finally the complete experiment was carried out and at once gave a positive result: when the source of neutrons bombarded the uranium, the interior surface of the Bakelite cylinder collected a complex mixture of radioactive atoms. As the internal diameter of the Bakelite cylinder was increased, a point was reached at which no radioactive material was deposited. This gave a measure of the range in air of these fission fragments.

On January 26, 1939, this experiment was successfully carried out by Joliot in less than half an hour. It had barely been completed when Joliot turned to Lew Kowarski and said to him: "I am sure that at this moment there must be many physicists who have already done the same thing."

It was a natural reaction at a time when the idea seemed too obvious to have escaped other people. But it was too modest a reaction, for only one physicist, O. R. Frisch, at Copenhagen, had thus far demonstrated the fission of the uranium atom—only a few days before, in fact, using a different method. Once he had obtained his result Frisch wrote to Niels Bohr, who was at that time in New York. On January 26, 1939, Niels Bohr described to the American Physical Society the details and results of the experiments carried out in Copenhagen. According to eyewitness accounts this announcement caused the hasty exit of a number of physicists in the direction of their laboratories. . . .

On January 30, 1939, a paper was presented to the Académie des Sciences of the Institut de France. In March, Joliot published an article in the *Journal de Physique*. In this he states:

The kinetic energy of the projected atoms is sufficient for them to penetrate a thin layer of uranium and to be deposited on a support. The presence of the atoms deposited will be revealed by their radioactivity. It is by this method that I was able to give an experimental proof of the splitting of uranium when bombarded by neutrons.

In addition to this Joliot repeated his experiments making use of the cloud chamber, and produced the first photograph of the trajectory of a fission fragment.

We have not yet reached the end of the road. We are only on the threshold of an adventure in which Joliot will play the rôle of precursor.

In his article in the *Journal de Physique* in March, 1939, the following short sentence occurs:

However, it is possible, if the excitation of the nuclei formed is sufficient, for several neutrons to evaporate. This last point is one of the most important and we have carried out experiments on this subject.

This point is crucial. When *one* neutron provokes the fission of one uranium nucleus a great amount of energy is liberated. If at the same time other neutrons are also liberated, these could in their turn cause more fissions and so on. There was thus a real possibility of seeing the start of "transmutations" of an explosive character, genuine chemical chain reactions, which Joliot had already foreseen in 1935 at the end of his Nobel Prize lecture.

The difficulty lay in having to distinguish between incident neutrons and those resulting from fission. At the beginning of February, 1939, Hans Halban proposed a "quantitative" experiment to study the numbers of neutrons. Lew Kowarski recommended a qualitative method which would make it possible to distinguish between the neutrons from their velocities. The two experiments were carried out and it was in their planning and execution that the team was formed which would work together first at the Collège de France, then at Ivry, and then at Clermont-Ferrand.

By the beginning of April, 1939, the demonstration had been made: in the course of splitting the uranium nucleus more than one neutron per fission was emitted. The chain reaction had definitely become a possibility which could be realized.

This number of neutrons—which for many years remained one of the best-kept military secrets—was estimated by the French team at about 3.5: the number accepted today is 2.5. Having reached this stage it remained to perfect the equipment which would make it possible to initiate and then to control a chain reaction. The first experimental arrangement tried by the team led by Joliot gave encouraging results: a subcritical chain reaction was produced—but not, so far, a self-sustaining one.

The prospects opened up by this series of discoveries were considerable and did not escape the attention of people with foresight. They covered not only the scientific, but also the industrial and military fields.

The international situation, which was growing more and more tense, could not fail to pose grave problems for all those who were involved at the heart of the initial development of atomic energy. Some of them even went so far as to consider that, if research into it could not be stopped, all publication of results should be suspended.

As early as February 2, 1939, Léo Szilard had written to Joliot from New York asking him not to publish the results of his research into the fission of uranium. Two months later a telegram of a hundred and forty words was sent again from New York, this time from V. Weisskopf to Hans Halban, making the same suggestion.

In principle the scientist is hostile to any kind of secrecy with regard to fundamental research. International scientific cooperation is an essential condition of scientific progress and cannot be reconciled with secrecy. Thus Joliot, in disagreement with Szilard, continued to publish.

But there was another problem, apart from the question of secrecy—that of the protection of eventual industrial applications. Joliot had frequently had the opportunity of discussing this question with Marie Curie who had presented a report to the League of Nations on the "Rights of Scientists." Pierre and Marie Curie had had to consider the question of patents at the time when the radioactive elements were discovered; the decision they took at that time is reported as follows in Marie Curie's book:

In this circumstance Pierre Curie adopted the most disinterested and liberal attitude. With my full agreement he renounced any attempt to reap material profit from our discovery. We consequently did not take out any patent and published, without any reserve, all the results of our research, as well as the processes used for the preparation of radium. In addition we gave anyone who was interested all the information he sought. This greatly benefited the radium industry which was able to develop quite freely, first in France and then abroad, and to provide scientists and doctors with the products they required.

Frédéric and Irène Joliot-Curie had adopted exactly the same attitude in relation to artificially radioactive elements. But in this case new considerations intervened. Who could guarantee that France would preserve the considerable lead she had at that time in this new field of atomic energy? (At that time the number of people who used that expression which is so common today could be counted on the fingers.) This consideration won the day and the decision was taken with the agreement of Francis Perrin, Lew Kowarski, and Hans Halban to take out five patents on the construction and utilization of atomic piles. Three of these patents were in the names of Joliot, Halban, Kowarski, and Perrin. Two were just in the names of Joliot, Halban, and Kowarski. The ownership of these patents was immediately transferred by the inventors to the C.N.R.S., which finally transferred them to the French Atomic Energy Commissariat (C.E.A.). In addition, on October 30 a sealed document was deposited at the Académie des Sciences in Paris. It was opened in 1949. Signed by Joliot, Halban, and Kowarski, it dealt with "the possibility of producing in a medium containing uranium an unlimited nuclear chain reaction." Thus both the general interest and their concern for the independence of France were safeguarded, while the scientists themselves had maintained their tradition of disinterestedness.

On March 8, 1948, an official document was to recognize these facts. In a letter to Frédéric Joliot-Curie, the President of the Conseil d'Etat, Monsieur Robert Schuman, wrote:

For all that, your decision certainly represents a sacrifice: it testifies once more, and in a brilliant fashion, to the extent of your disinterestedness and the depth of your patriotism. It is therefore my agreeable duty to thank you in the name of France.

Thus in 1939 France was ahead of every other country in work on the possible liberation and utilization of atomic energy. This is recognized, for example, by P. M. S. Blackett.[16]

Unfortunately France was to be submerged for four years by occupation, darkness, and betrayal. Defeat separated the members of the Collège de France team, but for a further two years Halban and Kowarski were to continue in Britain the work they had started with Joliot in execution of his direct instructions and under his recognized authority.

We shall have occasion to return to the progress of this work.

[16] *Biographical Memoir: F. Joliot,* November, 1960, p. 64.

Reading the titles of Frédéric Joliot's scientific publications allows one to confirm that we have here attempted only to describe, in the context of the evolution of scientific research, the main work of this scientist. In this list there are also to be found publications on biological subjects. Joliot immediately realized, upon discovering artificially radioactive elements, how greatly atoms made radioactive, and consequently identifiable in the tiniest doses, could be of service to biological research. In 1939, with A. Lacassagne, P. Sue, J.-P. Lablond, and Chamorra, he used radio-iodine to trace the fixation of iodine to the thyroid gland of rats, following the amputation of the hypophysis. In 1940 he created a biological section at the Atomic Synthesis Laboratory and it was indeed chiefly in this direction that he himself would have liked to concentrate. His research on the fission of uranium prevented him from doing so.

In a paper he wrote he presented the thoughts that had been inspired by his experiments in this field, which was a new one for him.

In a general way this biological research showed us how necessary it is to have close collaboration between researchers in different disciplines, complementing one another. It is not simply a question of the physicist giving advice on this or that physical technique: he must actually contribute to the science of biology, without laying claims to competence in this field, but with a view to bringing to it a different way of thinking, which can with benefit supplement the fundamental thinking of the biologist.

During and after the war he again undertook and achieved success in a number of biological studies with A. Lacassagne, R. Courrier, and Horeau, studies dealing with the metabolism of iodine and also with the first radio-cancers to be produced in rabbits by means of neutrons. One of his last pieces of experimental work concerned a highly expert opinion required by a court in a notorious arsenic poisoning case.

He was so naturally attracted by problems of this type that in the course of a long period spent in the Saint-Antoine hospital in 1955 he carefully studied the methods used by the doctors and on leaving the hospital submitted a memorandum suggesting notable improvements in these methods. The utterly scientific vigor with which over a period of three years he followed the course of his illness, the effect of the remedies, etc., contributed greatly to a partial recovery, which made it impossible to foresee the sudden end which came in August, 1958.

4

The Man and His Age

ALTHOUGH he devoted the greater part of his time to scientific research and teaching, Frédéric Joliot also interested himself, during the few years which preceded the outbreak of the Second World War, in political, economic, and social questions.

At the invitation of the Academy of Sciences of Leningrad, he made a trip to the U.S.S.R. in September, 1933. There he saw and studied many things. He was happy to meet again his colleague and friend Dmitri Skobeltsin, and he had conversations with many Soviet colleagues. But though his opinions were undeniably progressive, he had not yet committed himself. He had not felt it necessary to launch into public action.

The uprising of February 6, 1934, showed him that it was no longer possible, without being a coward, to remain a passive spectator. The workers' resistance on February 9 and 12 had held the Fascists in check but it was necessary to draw the moral from this and to pursue and develop a course of action.

The French intellectuals rallied around the philosopher, Alain, and the men of science, Paul Langevin and Paul Rivet. Frédéric Joliot joined their number. He was present at the Rue Las Casas in Paris at the inaugural meeting of the "Comité d'action antifasciste et de vigilance." Langevin deliberately wished to avoid using the word "intellectual" in the name of this committee. But the press and public opinion, faced with an association of intellectuals, would have altered their title and it was finally under the name of the "Comité de vigilance des intellectuels antifascistes" (The Vigilance Committee of Anti-Fascist Intellectuals) that the struggle was waged, and with which Frédéric Joliot effectively associated himself, not only attending the meetings of the committee and signing appeals, but also putting up posters and speaking in public on a number of occasions. In 1936 he was invited to talk about his recent discoveries and their possible future development to the "People and Culture" circle at Grenoble. He spoke first about the current crisis in science.

There is not a month, sometimes not a week in which we are not surprised by some important result. Rarely has science been as alive, and there are many men of science who have been momentarily troubled by this. Is not our generation still under the impression that science is something cut and dried and dead, an impression due to the dogmatic way in which we were taught facts and laws and in which, unhappily, our children are still being taught?

Then he turned to the problem of the use which is made of science:

The man in the laboratory, the scientist, studies natural phenomena from a purely disinterested point of view. Before undertaking a piece of research he does not care whether it will be useful or not. The engineer, the technician selects from among the discoveries made by the research worker and invents an apparatus or a machine which men can use. It is here, at the moment of utilization, which is generally done by yet a third category of individuals, that the grave errors are often committed. A certain machine, which ought to bring about a reduction in the hours worked by the worker, instead quickly causes unemployment. And everyone always makes science responsible, when it is in fact those who make bad use of it who should be blamed.

Joliot was very impressed by the pertinence of a great number of the questions with which he was bombarded after his lecture. And he also made the acquaintance of the organizer of the circle, Yves Farge, the writer, journalist, and painter, who was also in charge of the Vigilance Committee of Anti-Fascist Intellectuals for the department of Isère. The two men were to meet again frequently and the mutual sympathy they felt in the course of that evening developed into a firm friendship between the two great fighters for peace. Thus on April 4, 1953, it was Joliot who found the words with which to evoke at the funeral of Yves Farge the personality and the work of this great Frenchman.

In 1934 Joliot had joined the French Socialist Party, the S.F.I.O. and in 1936 the "League for the Rights of Man and of the Citizen" of which the president was Professor Victor Basch, who was assassinated during the Occupation by the men of the Vichy Government.

But after 1936 Joliot found himself in disagreement with the Socialist Party on the subject of the Spanish Civil War. Right from the beginning of Franco's rebellion, Frédéric Joliot committed himself categorically. He called for aid to Republican Spain and opposed the deceptiveness of the French official policy of "non-intervention," which in fact left the Fascist powers free to intervene, while denying the Spanish government the possibility of procuring the arms it needed.

After the capitulation at Munich in 1938, Frédéric Joliot ranged himself alongside Paul Langevin and all the intellectuals who denounced the hidden intentions of the signatories of the Pact and who sought to rally all the forces hostile to Hitlerism. He thus came to be a member of the delegation of intellectuals who called on the President of the French Republic, Albert Lebrun. With great emotion the members of this delegation told the President of their anxiety about the direction taken by French foreign policy, which was completely complaisant with regard to Hitler and Mussolini. Joliot was even moved to ask, very calmly but quite unequivocally, the question which was on the lips of all those present: "Has not the Minister for Foreign Affairs shown more than complaisance? Are we not faced with a complicity verging on treason?"

President Lebrun rose to his feet, outraged. He declared that he could not permit one of his ministers to be implicated in this way and curtly asked the delegation to withdraw.

Not long after this row Joliot delivered a lecture in the big lecture hall at the Sorbonne and in the presence of the President of the Republic. The subject was the medical application of artificially radioactive elements. At the end of this lecture the President came over to congratulate him and took him to one side and confided: "I was extremely fierce the other day. In the presence of so many people I could not have acted otherwise. But you were right!"

Frédéric Joliot was called up in 1939 as a captain of artillery and was put in charge of Group 1 of Scientific Research. Under a cover name, so as not to attract attention, the study of chain reactions continued. The first experiments and the theoretical studies showed that it was necessary to have a material which would slow down the neutrons which are ejected very rapidly when the uranium nucleus is split. Among the possible slowing-down or moderating materials was heavy water, of which a few favored laboratories possessed a few grams. At that time only one factory was extracting this precious substance from ordinary water by electrolysis: the factory belonging to the Norsk Hydro Company in Norway. Frédéric Joliot went to Raoul Dautry, the

Minister for Armaments, and obtained permission from him for all the heavy water available (twenty-six five-liter cans) to be bought in Norway and shipped to Paris with the greatest secrecy.

The world reserve of heavy water and a stock of uranium supplied to Joliot by the Union Minère of Katanga made it possible to continue the experiments on the fission of the uranium nucleus and its various applications. But events were not standing still. On May 16, 1940, Dautry sent for Joliot. The agents of the "Deuxième Bureau" (Military Intelligence) had already alerted Joliot several days before and expressed surprise at the incredulity they had encountered in official circles. Dautry now informed him that the French front had been broken at Sedan and that the Germans must be prevented at all costs from capturing the heavy water and even from discovering that such a considerable stock of it had been assembled in a French laboratory. The heavy water must at all costs be kept safe.

Joliot entrusted this confidential mission to the deputy director of his laboratory, his friend Henri Moureu. After a few preliminary soundings, Moureu managed to have the precious cans stored in the strong room of the Banque de France at Clermont-Ferrand where they were registered under the name of "Product Z."

In this town, which was considered to be less threatened than Paris, a villa, Clair Logis, was put at the disposal of Joliot and his colleagues, as a place to which they could move their equipment and continue their research. Another villa next to this one was available for living quarters and, three weeks after the decision to transfer, the experiments could continue.

But a few days later the director of the Banque de France expressed his desire to be rid of the twenty-six cans of the mysterious "Product Z." Henri Moureu, accompanied by J.-J. Trillat, returned to the Puy-de-Dôme area and on May 24, using a prearranged code language, he submitted a new proposal to Joliot by telephone, which Joliot approved. Thus it was that that the heavy water arrived in the cell reserved for dangerous criminals at the central prison at Riom. It was only kept in custody there for a short spell.

On June 10 and 11, 1940, Paris was suddenly empty. A black veil of smoke spread over the silent city in which the most fantastic rumors were circulating. The laboratories in which research for military purposes was being carried out received orders to withdraw southward. On June 11 the last crates of scientific equipment from Joliot's laboratory were shipped to Clermont-Ferrand.

In the deserted Collège de France Frédéric Joliot and Henri Moureu carefully sorted through the documents which related to the research on fission, the use of heavy water, etc. They personally took to Clermont-Ferrand only what was strictly indispensable. The rest was burned. No trace must be left which could give the Nazis an idea of the direction being taken in their current work. All this was scrupulously carried out . . . and all to no purpose whatsoever! For the periodic reports sent by Joliot to the Ministry for Armaments had been carefully sent off by this ministry in a railway carriage which was captured by the Germans at La Charité-sur-Loire. Joliot learned this some time later from the mouth of the German general himself when he came to visit Joliot's laboratory at the Collège de France.

On June 11 Frédéric and Irène Joliot got into their Peugeot 402 and left Paris for Clermont-Ferrand, followed a few yards behind by Henri Moureu in his 302. They were going to join Hans Halban, who had left at the end of May, and Lew Kowarski, who had left on June 5 and who had already started setting up a makeshift laboratory at the villa, Clair Logis.

On June 16, 1940, toward the end of the afternoon, Joliot and Moureu were taking a short walk on a road high above Clermont-Ferrand. The weather was fine, the countryside magnificent—everything tempted them to forget their worries. . . . But a car caught up with them and stopped beside them. The Secret-Service lieutenant who had successfully completed the operation with the heavy water took Joliot to one side. After a brief conversation Joliot returned to Moureu: "We must move on to Bordeaux."

They slept little at Clair Logis on the night of June 16. Joliot talked first to Halban, then to Kowarski, and it was decided that the two of them must leave for England, taking with them the heavy water, and put themselves at the disposal of the Allies. As for Joliot himself, he had not yet resolved what he should do. Once they had reached this decision, Joliot went on to comment on the news he had just received on the road. The forecast he made that night of the way events would go, would, if it were to be set down here, bear a strong resemblance, even in some details, to a "prediction" written after the event.

Early on the morning of June 17, Halban and Kowarski left for Bordeaux. They arrived at about midnight and received from Captain Bichelonne a handwritten directive, antedated the sixteenth, ordering them to embark on board the *Broompark,* which was flying the British flag. Frédéric, Irène, and Moureu then departed from Clermont-Ferrand. When they reached Clairville (Dordogne), the two men left Irène and went on to Bordeaux.

The Ministry of Armaments, which had withdrawn from Paris, was installed in one of the buildings of the Préfecture of the department of Gironde. It is there that Joliot and Moureu reported on the morning of June 18, 1940. On the threshold of the Préfecture they met Captain Bichelonne, the General Secretary of the Ministry of Armaments, who promised them all possible aid and did not conceal from them the extremity of the situation. It was not the first encounter between Joliot and this brilliant young and ambitious officer from the École Polytechnique. We shall see later that it was not to be the last. . . .

As Joliot and Moureu were climbing the stairs of the Préfecture, a man was coming down them. It was Lord Suffolk, delegate of the British War Office. Lord Suffolk, one of the rare people who knew of the research Joliot was doing, literally hurled himself upon him and said: "You are coming to England with me at once. Don't worry about your wife or your two children, I will be responsible for taking them to Brittany tomorrow and from there across the Channel. Everything has also been arranged for Halban and Kowarski who should by now be on board the *Broompark* with the cans of heavy water."

Joliot acquiesced with a gesture, while Moureu said nothing. A little later, Joliot, who wanted to see his colleagues again, went to the berth of the *Broompark*. But the berth had been changed and Joliot could not find out where the ship was. As Joliot was wandering about the docks, Halban and Kowarski were trying to obtain from Lord Suffolk, who had rejoined them, permission to go ashore before the ship sailed, in the hope of seeing their "chief" once more.

"Only the captain has the authority to give you permission," replied Lord Suffolk. "Go and ask him—but I am sure he will refuse you."

On the afternoon of June 18 the *Broompark* weighed anchor and made for the bay of Royan where a neighboring ship was to run into a mine. On the afternoon of the 19th they sailed for Southampton where they arrived on the 21st. Direct contact between Joliot and his team was not to be resumed again until a telephone conversation between London and Paris on January 12, 1946.

For their part Joliot and Moureu decided to go back to Irène. For a long time they sat silently side by side. Then Joliot voiced the doubt which was tormenting him.

"Should I accept Lord Suffolk's offer? The work must go on here."

"That's what I think," replied Moureu. "For you the position is not an easy one. To some extent you are a standard-bearer. . . ."

Again there was a silence. Then Joliot concluded: "I definitely ought to stay."

The invisible ties which bind one to the soil of one's native land had won the day. . . . Joliot had just made a decision which would involve him in a struggle the nature of which could in no way be foreseen at that time.

During the course of that conversation in which so few words were spoken, with such deliberation, which was so pregnant with consequences, what pictures flashed through his mind, what thoughts, what memories? One cannot be sure but one can guess. His children are in Brittany. His colleagues, apart from Halban and Kowarski, are dispersed. His master, Paul Langevin, is in Toulouse. Against the background of France massacred and cast adrift come memories and stories: his father during the Commune, his mother's parents in Alsace rebelling against Germanization, Marie Curie's memories of the people in Poland who fought for liberty. . . .

Those who took part in the start of the new academic year in occupied Paris in the autumn of 1940 are not likely to forget the extraordinary atmosphere. Those who did not experience it will doubtless find it hard to imagine.

The occupying power was still trying to win over the people and had not yet wielded the full weight of its forces of repression. Parisians went back to work utterly stunned by the collapse of the Republic and utterly amazed to find themselves alive in their city, which was virtually intact.

Activity was resumed but beneath the daily preoccupations of work and family everyone was questioning himself. There were certainly those who rejoiced at Hitler's victory and enjoyed the "divine surprise" of Charles Maurras. "Order" was to prevail and under the guidance of "the Marshal" a "revolution" was to take place which would be reassuring because it was "national." There were also those who from the first moment did not accept, and were resolved and determined to fight. Gradually they went into the shadows to set up the organization and gather arms for the Resistance. Then there were all the others who searched their consciences, hesitated, decided. And finally there were those who resolved in all circumstances to "wait" before choosing—and to adapt their attitude to the circumstances.

The Occupation authorities only very gradually revealed themselves in a tangible way—except for those who through their fame, their previous activity, or their position found themselves in exposed places.

The nuclear chemistry laboratory at the Collège de France was one of the first places to attract the attention of the German authorities, thanks to the discoveries which had been made there. Already in July, 1940, before Frédéric Joliot had returned to Paris, the soldiers of the Wehrmacht, accompanied by the physicist Bothe, had the laboratory opened in order to search for uranium, heavy water, or the results of experiments. The cyclotron at the Collège de France was also closely examined, but no one thought of going to the Atomic Synthesis Laboratory at Ivry.

In September, a few days after Joliot's return to Paris, the Germans visited the Collège de France once more. At their head was General Erich Schumann, who was in charge of scientific matters in the Wehrmacht (doubtless because he had once studied physics for a time and had subsequently written the music for several military marches). First there was a great seduction scene, in the course of which, in front of the flabbergasted laboratory workers, the general in uniform paid a "sparkling" tribute to the French scientist. The conversation which followed in Joliot's office was more to the point. Among those present on the German side there was even a genuine physicist, W. Gentner, whose anti-Nazi sentiments were well-known to the Frenchman whose words he had to interpret.

What interested the "visitors" most was what had happened to the heavy water and the uranium. Joliot replied that the heavy water had been put on an English ship at Bordeaux.

"What is the name of this ship?"

Joliot appeared to hesitate between the names of two ships, both of which, he knew, had been sunk.

"And the uranium?"

"Withdrawn by the Ministry for Armaments to an unknown destination."[1]

The German officer was shaken but not convinced and he afterward expressed his doubts to Gentner. "I think he told us that to reassure us, but it must all have been sent to North Africa. That is where we should send a mission."

Meanwhile Gentner, who had remained a few steps behind the others as they were leaving, managed to arrange a meeting with Joliot. At six o'clock the same evening at a café on the Boulevard Saint-Michel Joliot had his first secret meeting. There he learned that the Germans had decided to move into the Collège de France. Gentner, who had been asked to leave Heidelberg to come there, wanted to accept only if Joliot had no objection.

At Joliot's request, Gentner accepted the Paris post. He took part in discussions with the German authorities, at the end of which it was decided that four German research scientists should come to work in Paris. The negotiations were made much easier for Joliot by the information he had received from Gentner. At their conclusion Joliot was given a written guarantee by the proper authority which specified that he would remain the sole director of the laboratory, that only fundamental scientific research (i.e. non-military) would be carried out there, and that he would be kept fully informed of the progress of the work. Thus it was possible for the activity of this laboratory to start again. As time went by a good deal else besides physics came to be done there. Four years later, "Molotov cocktails" and wireless sets were being made in the rooms next to the ones where the Germans worked. W. Gentner, who was denounced by one of his compatriots,[2] was called back to Germany in 1942 and subsequently made only three brief visits to Paris. However, he came back immediately after the Liberation, equipped with false documents which had enabled him to leave the American zone. Joliot had had him supplied with the documents through a French military intelligence officer. At their first meeting after the fall of Hitler Joliot presented Gentner with a dark cubic block which was on his desk.

---

[1] A part of the stock of uranium, hidden, in fact, near Toulouse, was seized at the Liberation by the American authorities.

[2] The Americans later discovered a Gestapo report in which Gentner is accused of having democratic ideals, "probably influenced by his Swiss wife."—*Alsos, the Failure in German Science*, by Samuel A. Goudsmit, (London: Sigma Books, 1947), p. 190.

"But that is uranium produced by the 'Metallgesellschaft' works!" exclaimed Gentner. "How did it get here?"

"A French workman in Germany managed to take it and brought it to me when he came on leave."

Everything that happened in occupied Europe which might have any bearing at all on atomic energy was very closely watched by the intelligence services of the U.S. The information they received in 1940 is reported as follows (page 9 in S. Goudsmit's book, *Alsos,* which constitutes a document of the first importance):

French colleagues who escaped shortly after the fall of France had told us about the German interest in the famous French laboratory for nuclear physics, under the direction of the foremost French physicist, Frédéric Joliot-Curie, the son-in-law of Madame Curie. We learned that a German general had come to Paris with the intention of removing all the important apparatus to Germany. Later on it was decided to leave the equipment in place and send German scientists to work at the Paris laboratory.

There was another French scientist who could not fail to attract the attention of the Nazi occupying forces: Paul Langevin. On October 30, 1940, he was arrested, taken to Santé Prison and incarcerated in one of the cells for common criminals. The outrage provoked by this arrest was considerable. From Switzerland, the U.S.A., and the U.S.S.R. messages were sent to the German authorities offering asylum to Langevin. On November 8 Langevin would have given the first lecture of his annual course in Paris. The Resistance invited people to go to the Collège de France. The German authorities had had the Physics lecture room locked. Joliot went to the administrator and came back with the keys. The friends and pupils of the imprisoned scientist were able to take their places on the benches. Notable among them was Langevin's son-in-law, the brilliant young physicist Jacques Solomon, who was shot by the Nazis at Mont-Valérien (near Paris) on May 23, 1942. When Joliot took the Master's place before the blackboard and addressed the audience briefly, the emotion was intense. He had difficulty in speaking, for, like all those present, he was deeply upset. He stigmatized the assault which had been committed against a great Frenchman and against science and told his listeners of his decision to close his laboratory until Langevin was liberated. This decision did not concern him exclusively. It affected French and German scientific workers alike.

Conscious of the significance of what had happened, the audience left the Collège de France in complete silence.[3]

Joliot's position at that time was particularly delicate. He was in the occupied zone of Paris. German scientists were working in his laboratory. Some of his colleagues in the so-called "free zone" of Paris rapidly concluded that he was "collaborating." He could not have denied this without deliberately going underground. The time for this step would come, but later. For the moment Joliot simply began to make contact with colleagues like J. Wyart, Cavailles, J. Nicole, J. Solomon, E. Aubel, and others.

On May 15, 1941, an appeal from the underground Communist Party was circulated at the University. This called for the creation wherever possible of National Front Committees to fight the occupying power by all means, including the setting up of armed groups. In June, 1941, a committee of this kind was set up at the University of Paris and Joliot figured among its members. The National Front gradually developed throughout France, a national committee was set up and Frédéric Joliot-Curie was elected president. In this way he came to know the architect, Pierre Villon, and somewhat later, Laurent Casanova.

Then began the long series of secret meetings, the place of which had to be constantly changed. The organization of meetings which today would take a good secretary less than an hour to arrange called for long and dangerous work by the comrades who kept people informed, who agreed to act as messengers, risking their lives each time: consciously and inconspicuously. Notable participants at these meetings were Henri Wallon, Francis Jourdain, Fr. Philippe, Mgr. Chevrot, Pierre Lebrun, the trade unionist, General Dassault, Jacques Debu-Bridel, among others.

At a time when so many members of the would-be élite in France had bowed their heads or prostrated themselves at the feet of the occupying powers or their servants, it was comforting for hundreds of thousands of citizens to learn— through the countless mysterious channels of information

---

[3] As a consequence of this protest and many others, Langevin's treatment in prison was slightly improved. He was given paper and pencils, which enabled him to work. Thirty-eight days later he was moved to a house under guard in Troyes, where Joliot often went to see him. The theoretical work Langevin had done in Santé Prison was confiscated. He was given a copy and Colonel Boehmelburg of the Gestapo kept the originals.

which come into existence in an occupied country—that some, at least, had not surrendered.

In the spring of 1942, the war seemed likely to continue for many years. The German armies were victorious over the Soviet Union. Frédéric Joliot took then a decision which he had considered at length. He was fully aware of its importance and it was to exercise a considerable influence on his life. At the moment when Jacques Solomon was executed he applied to Pierre Villon to join the French Communist Party. He was accepted at once. His membership remained secret until August 31, 1944.

Seven years had passed since his return from Stockholm, during which Frédéric Joliot had seen numerous official responsibilities entrusted to him, while his authority and fame increased both in France and abroad. At forty-six and in full possession of his intellectual and physical capacities, he was in a position to lead an active and happy life. He had a comfortable house at Antony, where he lived with his wife and two children, Hélène and Pierre. The laboratory, where he was in charge of a considerable team of research workers, could by itself easily satisfy his great capacity for work.

In addition to this, both before the war and also since the Nazi occupation, requests had come repeatedly from industrial groups who sought the collaboration—well paid and far from strenuous—of this young and brilliant scientist. Many boardroom doors were opened to him—all he had to do was to cross the threshold. Later on he pictured, without the least regret, the comfortable and conformist road he could have traveled—and which he rejected without hesitation at the time.

At the back of his decision were his love for France and his determination to do everything in his power to insure that this great and fair country be able to offer to the civilization of tomorrow—the one which would flourish once Nazism had been conquered—a contribution worthy of what it had been in the past. On many occasions he explained: "I became a Communist because I am a patriot."

He could conceive of the struggle to be waged against the occupying power, and the one to be continued after the victory, only as one fought shoulder to shoulder with other men, one in which each man draws strength from his contact with the others and in ceasing to be isolated. In a speech made in April, 1950, at the Twelfth Congress of the French Communist Party at Gennevilliers, he was to describe in the following manner how he had come to make his choice:

But in the intimacy which one finds in action, sustained by the mutual respect which is established between brave and honest men of differing opinions and professions who are all working for a noble end, the Communist, by his example and by the explanations he gives to the problems which puzzle and worry his companions, brings them an understanding of the immense human value of communism and the way it upholds and liberates those who serve it. It is in this way that I came to join our great Party and tens and thousands of others have taken the same road.

I am convinced that, like me, they are infinitely grateful in their hearts to their elders who have enlightened them.

Fighting and driving out the invader, working for the France of tomorrow—these were the tasks to which Frédéric Joliot devoted himself in the company of his comrades in the Resistance. These tasks had many aspects but they had one characteristic in common: danger.

Joliot presided over the meetings of the "Front National" and coordinated the action of personalities as diverse as François Mauriac, Pierre Villon, and Fr. Philippe. But there were opportunities for direct action which could not be neglected or delegated to others. It was quite natural for Joliot to go and see Henri Moureu, who was now in charge of the police headquarters laboratory and who was required, in this capacity, to investigate all cases of sabotage and to impound the unexploded devices and all the weapons parachuted by the English. A few conversations sufficed to create an embryo underground organization. Thus a valuable chain for the redistribution of materials was formed, starting at police headquarters and passing via the Collège de France to the direct action groups. A few visits to the police laboratory; a few lunches near the Gare de Lyon, in the Rue des Écoles or near the Théâtre de l'Odéon; a parcel changing hands; and the explosives were once more ready to be used.

The information obtained by Moureu and passed on by Joliot was often very valuable, as the following story shows. The Germans were making full use of the air-liquefaction plant at Boulogne-Billancourt. A group of Francs-Tireurs and partisans were sent to blow up the factory. They easily succeeded in overpowering the night watchman, laying the plastic charges, setting fire to the delayed action fuses, and getting away in time. But nothing happened! Moureu, who was sent by the police to investigate, discovered that in laying the fuses the group had been careless enough to leave contacts unconnected. He told Joliot. A week later the factory was blown up.

At that time all young Frenchmen faced the possibility of being sent to Germany for forced labor. Joliot joined the struggle against forced labor. To this end in the middle of the war he created the company SEDARS (Société d'études des applications des radio-éléments artificiels). The director of this company was Professor Léon Denivelle who was later to become the first Secretary General of the French Atomic Energy Commissariat. Thanks to this company, Joliot was able to raise some money to pay scientific workers and thus provide them with the indispensable "work certificates." But this experiment had an added significance and provided a valuable example. In so far as the political and social régime in France would remain unchanged after the war, it would be essential to arrange for the resumption of industrial activity within the framework of this régime with the maximum speed and efficiency. It would therefore be necessary to have cooperation between the people running private industry, the scientists, the technicians, and the state. And this cooperation could only be healthy and fruitful if the positions of each were clearly defined and mutually understood. During the war SEDARS remained an extremely small company but Joliot foresaw great development for it in the future. He had occasion to talk to many of the men of power in the regime at that time, who remained in power after the war. Meeting one of them in 1943, an important banker, the brother of a minister in the Vichy government, Joliot began the interview by making his position clear:

"I do not share your opinions. You are a capitalist and I am a technician. I know your capitalist system and I reject it. You cannot contradict me when I speak of board meetings at which members go in and out to give orders to their brokers as a result of information they have just received.

"I do not know what will happen to you after the defeat of Germany. Perhaps you will be shot.

"Nevertheless we ought to be able to examine together the best conditions for insuring that the country make effective use in industry of scientific and technical progress."

As soon as the captain of industry had realized that the man addressing him in this way was not susceptible to the usual "arguments" and that by virtue of his science and his character he represented an undeniable force, it was perfectly possible for a dialogue to be established between them.

For want of capital, SEDARS did not survive the Occupation long but the experience Joliot had gained from the different contacts he made was extremely valuable to him, and he later drew on it when he tried to bring about the collaboration between the French Atomic Energy Commissariat and French industry—a collaboration necessary despite there being no question whatsoever of the latter determining the policy of the former, either from without or from within.

Among the many projects which the French, concerned about the future of their country, planned during the long night of the Occupation, the reform of the educational system occupied a prominent place. The General Committee on Education had asked Joliot to prepare a scheme for the reform of higher education. Once Joliot had produced a first plan he considered it necessary to obtain the opinion of Paul Langevin, who had thought about this problem for many years. But Langevin, whose position at Troyes had become precarious, had been smuggled into Switzerland in an escape organized by Joliot and Denivelle. In order to avoid the risks of the mail or of sending a messenger, the following method was used. One very hot day in May, 1944, the secret transmitter which Denivelle had set up in the church tower at Montbéliard transmitted in Morse to its Swiss receiver at the top of the Roche d'Or not the usual military information but a memorandum on the reorganization of higher education in liberated France.

It was during this period that Joliot had his last encounter with Bichelonne. The latter was now the Minister of Industrial Production in the Vichy government and one of the most active collaborators with the Nazis. One Saturday morning Joliot had abandoned both physics and the Resistance for his favorite sport and was fishing on the Seine at Soisy-sous-Etiolles. From his boat he saw a black Citröen with insignia approaching. Then the proprietor of the restaurant near where he kept his boat signaled to him urgently to come back. Once ashore he learned that Bichelonne had had him traced and wished to see him at once. He was taken to see the Minister in his fishing clothes, without being given a chance to go and change.

Joliot must often have wondered afterward what motives could have driven Bichelonne to organize this rather surprising interview. In the Minister's chair sat a man who had staked his life on a German victory and who, since the defeat at Stalingrad, had been filled with doubts; in the visitor's chair, a scientist whose general attitude the Minister suspected, without being really certain. In the past these two men had had occasion to work together in obtaining heavy water, in stocking uranium, and then in evacuating the heavy water to England. Joliot knew that he faced an enemy, but his responsibility to the Resistance prevented him from revealing his feelings. So he contented himself with listening. And what he heard confirmed the view he had already formed about the motives of the Vichy quislings. Referring to the role of the élite in France after the war, Bichelonne made his position clear: "I have put my money on the victory of the Germans because this victory has already brought us order and will keep order for us. But if I have backed the wrong horse, if the Germans lose, then the Americans will come. We shall still have order and it will be possible to work with them. . . ."

As Joliot's underground activities took up more and more time it became impossible for him to continue to lead a normal existence. His wife and children were safe in Switzerland. He decided to "disappear." He had already used pseudonyms in the Resistance ("Euler" and then "Adrian"); now he adopted a false identity. Under the name of "Jean-Pierre Gaumont" he rented a ground-floor flat in Belleville* for 300 francs a month. On June 26, 1944, after dining with his friends the Ségals, he took the "métro" and moved into the place which was to be—for how long?—his home and refuge.

This altered existence was bound to cause an emotional reaction. Indeed for the first time in his life as far as is known, he was moved to keep a diary, from which several extracts are given here.

June 26, 1944 10 P.M.

Dinner with Marinette and Jo Ségal. As usual an excellent meal and a pleasant occasion. The children were there, also a friend of Pierre, Jean-Denis Faure, a young poster designer from the Atelier Colin. Pierre showed us several of Faure's designs. Excellent drawings, good ideas and color. We discussed painting, technique and sincerity. For me a work is necessarily a combination of the two. To create an impression of relief, of three dimensions while only using two, can only be achieved by means of techniques or devices, which are not to be despised. The use of red and blue to give certain objects depth and distance is extremely ancient but it

* *Translator's Note:* A district in the northeast of Paris.

seems as if most modern painters are unaware of this device, which was used by the Chinese and the painters of the Italian Renaissance. (Chinese: porcelain. Italians: religious paintings.) After dinner—journey by métro to the Place des Fêtes ... Belleville, a district which was completely unknown to me. I have to meet my landlady. What will she be like? Friendly or not? ... My landlady, Madame Demange, whom I have just met, works from morning till night in a paper mill in Montrouge. She is a small woman in her forties, typical Parisian working class. ...

Madame Demange came down and brought me a plate of fine cherries from her garden. There must be a garden somewhere, a few square yards skillfully used and a cherry tree. I should have doubted it, given the building density, but the cherries are a proof: they were delicious. This gesture put heart into me, for it is hard to be alone after so many happy years of family life. Once again I recognize a friendly and generous gesture from one of those who work ten hours a day. They are still capable of such gestures after ten hours of work which is often exhausting and enervating. ...

I finally went to sleep, or rather switched off the light and tried to sleep. It is notoriously difficult to sleep in a new bed, especially if one is in a new house. One is extremely sensitive, one notices all the little noises of the strange house—and the smells. The tap which will not switch off completely and drips every two minutes into the washbasin; the creaking of the furniture and the house as it cools during the night, etc. One has to become familiar with the noises of each particular house in order to achieve the repose necessary for sleep. I became familiar with these fairly quickly but there were quite subtle smells which held my attention. There was a dominating one which I had not noticed in my room that afternoon. (A proof of the considerably increased power of our senses in the state preceding sleep.) Doubtless this smell came from a disinfectant—cresyl or some such—and I suddenly recalled a similar smell in the bedroom my father died in and in the room where the coffin rested for a day and a half. I could not forget this smell and often when I smell it, the same image is vividly called to mind.

After a new plunge into the night I was wakened by the wailing of sirens—an air raid! I heard my neighbor dressing and hurrying downstairs. When the door opens and shuts it rings a bicycle bell. I heard her running down the street. She was probably going to the Place des Fêtes métro station, which is particularly deep. (The escalator is at least 25 yards long. It is still working despite the electricity cuts.) Half an hour later the all-clear sounded. I had heard several low-flying aircraft but no explosions. My landlady came in again and went back to bed.

It was also about that time that Joliot went to Lyon with R. P. Philippe and Laurent Casanova. They spent several days in hiding at the house of an Alsatian cousin of Joliot's, a woman who ran a pastry shop in Lyon, waiting to meet someone who would arrange for them to go to Algiers to join the "Consultative Assembly" there. But nothing happened and they went back to Paris. It was only on the day they left that they discovered with restrospective alarm that the cousin's fiancé was an active member of "Petain's militia"!

Then came the Paris rising. The Nuclear Physics and Chemistry Laboratory of the Collège de France specialized for the moment—and with great efficiency—in the preparation of explosives a good deal more primitive than the atomic bomb, but none the less effective against the tanks of the Wehrmacht.

The hour of liberty had sounded and the time of public responsibilities had begun.

5

Public Responsibilities

THE REORGANIZATION OF SCIENTIFIC RESEARCH

> I will state quite simply that if this country does not make the necessary effort to give science the importance it merits and to give those who serve it the prestige necessary for their influence to be felt, it will sooner or later become a colony.
>
> Frédéric Joliot-Curie (1945)

PARIS WAS LIBERATED. Soon the whole of France would be free. The downfall of Fascism had become a certainty. After that it would be both necessary and possible to solve all the vital problems involved in reconstructing and reviving the country. Under the Occupation they had analyzed and confronted problems and prepared solutions. The French nation was ready to get down to work and hopes ran high.

Henri Wallon, the Commissioner for National Education, asked Frédéric Joliot-Curie to become the director of the National Center for Scientific Research (Centre National de la Recherche Scientifique, the "C.N.R.S."). René Capitant, when he became Minister of National Education, confirmed this appointment. In February, 1945, Professor Georges Teissier was appointed deputy director and was associated with the planning and putting into effect of reforms, before himself becoming director when Joliot left for the French Atomic Energy Commission.

When the new director of the C.N.R.S. entered the building at 13 Quai Anatole France, he was entering an institution with whose history, achievements, and insufficiencies he was already familiar.

If one reviews the history of the efforts made to insure that the scientific research carried out in France be worthy of a great country, one leading figure emerges: that of Jean Perrin, a great scientist who was also a poet, and whose tireless energy succeeded in overcoming much hesitation and skepticism. There is one date, too, that stands out for the historian: 1936. In that year the Popular Front government had sought to mark the importance it attached to scientific research by creating, for the first time, a government department especially responsible for it. Thus under Jean Zay as Minister for National Education, first Irène Joliot-Curie, and then Jean Perrin became Under Secretaries of State for Scientific Research.

At the end of 1944, before they could embark on reforms and new development, there was another task which had to be given priority: that of fully involving scientific workers in the struggle against Hitler's Germany. Joliot undertook this with his usual energy and did everything necessary to insure that his own workers were inspired with the same desire for success.

But the public authorities had also to be persuaded and in particular the Finance Minister, ". . . who, thanks to an absurd public policy, which had been pursued for years, did not understand what an excellent investment for the country scientific and technical research constituted." (Lecture at the 17th cycle of studies of the C.E.G.O.S., 1945)

His authority as a scientist and his courageous attitude during the Occupation[1] permitted him to win a triumph of which he was always very proud. When the annual budget was being discussed Joliot was called in by the Finance Minister. The credit he wanted for the C.N.R.S. represented a 200 percent increase on the previous allocations. The budget director was sitting beside his Minister "with scissors in hand." In a few sentences Joliot explained the national importance of the C.N.R.S. and justified his proposals. "Credits granted" concluded the Minister. His director looked horrified!

It was essential for the C.N.R.S. to be reformed. After detailed studies, carried out in collaboration with expert commissions, Frédéric Joliot-Curie and Georges Teissier drew up the statute[2] which still determines the main lines on which scientific research is organized in France.

It is absolutely characteristic of Joliot's outlook that the

---

[1] At the Liberation he was made Commandeur de la Légion d'honneur for military services and awarded the Croix de Guerre.

[2] Ordonnance 45-2632 of November 2, 1945 (Journal Officiel, November 3, 1945, p. 7913).

first measure of reorganization which he discusses in his introduction, which explains why this statute is needed, should be one devoted to the young. His experience as director of two laboratories had enabled him to see at first hand the insufficiency of the training given to the graduates in the science faculties and the engineers from the big schools when they undertook specialized research. The statute therefore provided for the establishment of "training preparatory to research":

Thus young research workers on the threshold of their careers will benefit from a training much more complete then they could receive by spending periods abroad at various research centers. Finally by giving guidance to the interested students when they are choosing their options, the Center will contribute to a better distribution of research workers in the different branches of science and technology.

It was also essential to give fair career prospects to those who wanted to devote themselves entirely to scientific research. To this end a correlation was established between the grants paid by the C.N.R.S. and the salaries paid to those in higher education.[3]

The C.N.R.S. was not to be an anonymous administrative body divorced from the workers in the laboratories. A "National Committee for Scientific Research" was set up "in order to associate with the life of the Center the most representative scientists and scientific research workers of France." A directorate drawn from the National Committee was to insure that the C.N.R.S. continue to be run in the interests of science.

The former structure of the C.N.R.S. had differentiated between pure and applied research. The new reforms abolished this distinction and thus "testified to the continuity which exists between pure science and all its applications."

Finally Joliot also attacked the problem of coordinating research between the numerous government departments which possess their own research services. There was no question of abolishing these, but the C.N.R.S. could play an important role in the exchange of information, above all in helping to avoid duplication of work. Joliot discussed this problem with the then Vice President of the Conseil, Maurice Thorez. The latter decided to create a specialized interdepartmental commission which did excellent work but did not succeed in overcoming departmental parochialism.

[3] Decree of August 12, 1945, modified on November 17, 1946.

In connection with the various statutory texts he had to produce and the reforms undertaken, Joliot came to read a passage which made him ask himself many questions about the difficulties which stand in the way of the implementation of the ideas of even the greatest minds.

When I was directing the C.N.R.S., taking into account the previous fifteen years of its existence, I had to produce reports outlining a new structure and orientation for this body. I thought I had found an original solution but shortly afterward I chanced to read several memoirs of Pasteur who had proposed similar solutions seventy years before. There is no doubt that if attention had been paid to Pasteur the development of French science and technology would have been great facilitated. It is likely that even before Pasteur similar ideas had been formulated.

What were Joliot's ruling ideas when he was the director of the C.N.R.S.? He has spoken of them so often himself that it is not difficult to answer this question.

First of all there was the fact that thriving and fruitful scientific research was fundamental not only to the educational but also to the industrial development of the country. Nations depend on the progress made by science and technology more and more. If one wanted to safeguard the independence of France—and Joliot wanted this passionately —it was necessary for France to make her own contribution to the general advancement of knowledge. In the modern world to renounce scientific creativity is to abandon one's country to overt or disguised colonization.

In addition to this there was the fact that scientific research takes on multiple forms which are conventionally divided into two categories: "pure" and "applied" research. Joliot rebelled against this arbitrary division and insisted on the point that very often the work of "pure science" sooner or later has important industrial applications. This is yet another reason for rejecting the mirage of concentrating only on immediately useful research. During his visit to the U.S.S.R. in his conversations with the authorities of that country, which was then in the midst of a period of industrialization, he had insisted on the importance of fundamental research. He had been listened to and understood.

One day a journalist[4] said to him: "You put great emphasis on 'fundamental research.' Could you give us a definition?" Joliot replied:

[4] *Gazette de Lausanne,* June 29, 1957

Fundamental research is the study of phenomena in themselves, without any concern about industrial application. But you should also notice that there is no example of a scientific discovery which has not, sooner or later, found a practical application.

And he continued his statement, giving free rein to his imagination, with a sketch of a "pure research worker" which is a veritable "self-portrait":

Above all, you must not think that I wish to establish a classification which would put pure research workers in a kind of aristocracy. [Monsieur Joliot-Curie smiled.] Every human activity calls for particular qualities. But those which one likes to find in fundamental research are close to those which favor artistic creation: a sure grasp of basic techniques and solid craftsmanship (Van Gogh was not an inspired dauber—he had learned his craft meticulously) at the service of a creative imagination and intuition. The conditions of work will be less rigid than those for industrial research, which necessarily have to be subject to fixed norms. A pure researcher can be suddenly inspired and work sixteen hours at a stretch, knowing that he can make this up the next day. We should arrange flexible schedules which take account of individual needs. It is not a question of indulging idleness or anarchy, but of having confidence in men and women who have proved their worth.

I am thinking of those Arab artists who make mosaics and carve ceilings. They spend hours listening to music and drinking mint tea (they have an orchestra provided for them) and then suddenly they leap onto their ladders and work without stopping for "a night and a day . . . and then fall back into their meditation."

Monsieur Joliot-Curie paused. Then he added:

I am always busy and I have sometimes told myself that if I had taken time off to meditate a little about my work I could have avoided wasting time in the case of several experiments.

Joliot found a definition of what the true research worker's aim should be in this extract from Paul Langevin's report to the "Commission on the Reform of Education":[5]

It is by developing the aptitudes of the individual as completely as possible and by then putting the human being, thus enriched, at the service of humanity that the double duty to one's personality and to human solidarity is fulfilled. It is this double duty that I, for my part, conceive to be the essence of all human morality.

[5] *La Pensée*, November-December, 1944, pp. 25-31.

Among the conditions which must permit this personality to find its full expression, working conditions, environment, and tradition all play an important part and any organization for scientific research must take care not to disregard their importance.

"I should like," he said one day,[6] "to draw attention to a fact which seems to me important: in new laboratories money and technical means are not enough by themselves to establish the necessary conditions for scientific research.

"In the old labs there are hidden riches composed of traditions and of an intellectual and moral capital accumulated from conversations, from teaching and from a certain presence. At a given moment all these elements can create the conditions indispensable for the emergence of the correct interpretation of a discovery. The best way to explain this is with an example: that of the neutron.

"In 1923 Rutherford had already used this word in one of his lectures at the Cavendish Laboratory, when he put forward the hypothesis that the existence of a neutral particle, which together with protons constituted the nucleus, might be possible. In 1930 Bothe and Becker discovered an extremely penetrating form of radiation. Irène Joliot-Curie and I repeated their experiments in 1932 and demonstrated the effect of the collision of nuclei with this radiation. As a result of these discoveries Chadwick succeeded in detecting the electrically neutral particles, capable of great penetration, to which he gave the name of neutrons. It was only natural for this point, which emerged from a series of experiments, to be finally established at the Cavendish Laboratory where Chadwick had worked with Rutherford and had absorbed the teachings of his master.

"In the same way it was only natural for artificial radioactivity to be discovered at the Radium Institute in Paris where the conditions were most favorable. We had large sources of polonium there at our disposal. With Pierre Curie, Marie Curie had discovered naturally radioactive elements there, and, thanks to her teaching, we had a perfect understanding of them. There was thus a tradition there, which, when we were faced with a phenomenon, could produce in us immediate reflexes, *radioactivists'* reflexes."

At the end of 1945 the C.N.R.S. was in full swing. Its director was now to be summoned to undertake another mission.

[6] *Gazette de Lausanne,* June 29, 1957.

> Give men the opportunity to accomplish something they want to do, offer them a constructive goal and they will be capable of breaking records. That is how ZOE, the first atomic pile, was completed in two and a half years: *thanks to the faith of a whole team.*
>
> Frédéric Joliot-Curie.

IN THE spring of 1940 the French scientists had made considerable progress toward the liberation of atomic energy. Their calculations were kept secret, like those of Szilard, Fisk, and Shockley, but, to quote P. M. S. Blackett's[7] opinion once more: "There is little doubt that, had the war not intervened, the world's first self-sustaining chain reaction would have been achieved in France."

On June 18 the *Broompark* was preparing to sail for England. Halban and Kowarski were on board. The cans of heavy water lay in the hold. But they took with them more than this rare and precious liquid. They had been given precise instructions for the continuation of their work first at Cambridge and then at Chalk River in Canada. The British Government statement, issued on August 12, 1945, describes their work in these words:

Drs. Halban and Kowarski were instructed by Professor Joliot to make every effort to get in England the necessary facilities to enable them to carry out, with the cooperation of the British Government, and in the joint interest of the Allies, a crucial experiment which had been planned in Paris and for which the heavy water had been acquired. Facilities were provided at the Cavendish laboratory, Cambridge, and by December, 1940, they produced strong evidence that in a system composed of uranium oxide (as actually used) or uranium metal with heavy water as the slowing-down medium, a divergent slow-neutron fission chain reaction would be realized if the system were of sufficient size.

On December 2, 1942, when, under the direction of Enrico Fermi, the first atomic pile went critical at Chicago University Stadium, Frédéric Joliot-Curie was unaware that the apparatus, the principles of which he and his colleagues had defined in several publications, including *Nature* in April,

[7] Biographical Memoir: Jean Frédéric Joliot, p. 96.

1939, and in the patents, had proved successful in operation, liberating immense sources of energy for man's use. There were, indeed, few men who knew what had happened.

In 1941 and 1942 Halban and Kowarski had several times explained to the English that it would be of the greatest possible value to make contact with Joliot. The point was noted but they heard no more about it.

Toward the end of 1943 Colonel Navarre, who was sent to France by the French Government in London, met Joliot and Denivelle in the course of a dinner in a restaurant in the Place Saint-André-des-Arts in Paris. He gave them some idea of the progress made by the Allies and invited Joliot to come to England secretly at intervals. Joliot agreed to this proposal, and from then on began to talk about the great measures it would be necessary to take in order to make up the time that had been lost. But, as it turned out, he never again heard any mention of the trips to England.

The more progress the Americans made toward the manufacture of the atomic bomb, the more anxious they became about what the Germans could have discovered. The "Alsos Mission," which was charged with discovering all possible information on this subject, accompanied the American armies of liberation. Here is the account of their investigations at the Collège de France[8]:

Colonel Pash entered Paris with the very first Allied troops. We civilians came two days later. Our first contact was naturally with the foremost French nuclear physicist, Joliot-Curie. His laboratory at the Collège de France had been making "Molotov cocktails" and other homemade explosives for the French Resistance. . . .

Joliot told us all he knew but after several conversations it was plain that he knew nothing of what was going on in Germany. He confirmed our previous information that two German high officials had visited him immediately after the Occupation, a Professor Erich Schumann and a Dr. Diebner. They wanted to remove the cyclotron and all other scientific equipment to their home laboratories. But later there was a change of plans and instead they sent physicists to work in the Paris laboratory.

It was the fact that German scientists were known to be working in his laboratory that gave rise to the rumors, current during the German occupation, that Joliot was a collaborationist. As it turned out, Joliot had very little to do with the Germans who had taken over his laboratory. Far from being a collaborationist, he was involved in the French underground Resistance movement.

[8] *Alsos, the Failure in German Science*, by S. A. Goudsmit, p. 34.

Another section of the Alsos mission, under the command of Colonel Chittick, included among its members the chemist W. Albert Noyes.[9] He has very kindly written me this account of his visit to the Collège de France in August, 1944:

I no longer remember the date, but it was a Sunday afternoon, two days after General Leclerc entered Paris. There were very few Americans there and our orders were to find Joliot-Curie. We therefore went straight to the Collège de France. I had been told that he had been in hiding for several months but we found him at the laboratory and he welcomed us warmly.

There was little to eat, we had only our rations, but that first night we had a real banquet in the laboratory. As we did not know where to go, we slept on the spot in camp beds. There was a German air raid on the north of Paris and one could hear gunfire in the distance. Apart from this a thunderstorm added its own note to the celebration.

We moved to a hotel the next day. Joliot told us about his experiences during the war, his life in the Resistance, and how he had made incendiary bombs on the laboratory benches.

Those days in Paris in August, 1944, are unforgettable.

It was during this period that Frédéric Joliot-Curie, W. A. Noyes, and Léon Denivelle met over dinner in the Latin Quarter. The idea of a French organization that would resume the work interrupted by the invasion of 1940 was born. . . .

But it was still too soon. The war was not over and the scientists must now play their part in it. Then scientific work had to be reorganized and Joliot was completely taken up with the running of the C.N.R.S. Meanwhile, however, his ideas about how to give France atomic energy were gradually crystallizing.

Having made official contacts in December, 1944, with the British authorities, and after further discussions with Irène Joliot-Curie, Raoul Dautry, Pierre Auger, and Francis Perrin, Joliot wrote to General de Gaulle during the autumn of 1945 to emphasize the importance of promoting research and industrial development in France, in order to follow up the discoveries made in the field of atomic energy in which French scientists had played such an important role. Joliot

[9] Professor W. A. Noyes had met Joliot several times before the war, at Arcouest, in Brittany, and at Coupeau (Haute-Savoie). Mrs. Noyes, who was a Frenchwoman by birth, had been a pupil at the Collège Sévigné in Paris at the same time as Irène Curie.

twice went to see the president of the provisional government and he obtained satisfaction on every point: the organization to be created—the French Atomic Energy Commission (Commissariat à L'Energie Atomique, the C.E.A.)—was to be directly under the President of the Conseil d'Etat and would not be subject to the meddlesome and multiform tutelage of the Ministry of Finance.

Joliot was to retain a very vivid memory of the two interviews he had with General de Gaulle and of the latter's understanding of the objectives to be attained and the scale of the effort which would be necessary—as well as their importance for the independence of France. Joliot listened, without being convinced, to the General's advice to him to behave like a somewhat mysterious and distant "leader," only rarely appearing among his colleagues in order to give them essential instructions. He would also refer, in describing those moments, to General de Gaulle's final words: "I have confidence in very few men. Joliot, I have confidence in you."

Installed in his office on the third floor of the fine building at 41 Avenue Foch, Paris,[10] the High Commissioner for Atomic Energy could take stock of the situation. In order to carry the burden of administrative work—which was to become heavier and heavier—he sought out Raoul Dautry, who was appointed Administrator-General, delegated by the government. His faithful friend Léon Denivelle was appointed Secretary General. General Dassault was responsible for liaison with the national defense ministries.

In 1945, Joliot explained in a lecture:[11]

We were in an extremely favorable position by comparison with other countries. France possessed the men who knew in detail how to construct atomic piles. These men, seven in number, were assembled at the C.E.A. and formed a "brain" which was conscious of its responsibility to the country and which would spare no effort to achieve success.

Who were the "six" who, in addition to Joliot, the High Commissioner, constituted the "brain" of the Commission? First there were the three commissioners, Irène Joliot-Curie, Pierre Auger, and Francis Perrin (the last two had returned from Canada and the U.S.A.).

Most important, there were Lew Kowarski, Bertrand Goldschmidt, and Jules Guéron who, with the agreement of

[10] The office was later moved to 69 Rue de Varenne in the seventh arrondissement.

[11] Lecture at the Versailles Prefecture March 8, 1947.

the British and American authorities, had returned to France to put themselves at Joliot's disposal. Hans Halban, for his part, had remained in Oxford. The experience this team had acquired during the war was to prove extremely valuable, avoiding a great deal of trial and error. To repeat an image of Lew Kowarski's, this experience represented the interest reaped on that initial capital of knowledge which Joliot had entrusted to his colleagues at the time when they left France in 1940.

Seated around a table together with Léon Denivelle and Jean Langevin, who took care of the secretary's office,[12] was the embryo of the "scientific committee"[13] which drew up the plans and recommended the decisions to be taken by the official responsible body, which was the "Atomic Energy Committee" presided over by the President of the Conseil.

The meetings of the scientific committee were frequent, often long, and punctuated by various incidents, sometimes comic or violent. All questions were discussed and in view of the diversity of the personalities and the violence with which opinions were sometimes expressed, the High Commissioner often needed all his patience, his skill, and his qualities as an organizer.

The plan laid down in 1946 was in three stages:

The first provided for the construction of a uranium and heavy water pile. At a press conference held in July, 1947, the High Commissioner announced: "By the end of 1948 one of the piles will certainly be completed." For during the course of the previous month the scientific committee, after discussing an idea put forward by Bertrand Goldschmidt and Bruno Pontecorvo, had decided to set about constructing a uranium oxide pile, using heavy water as a moderator. Even at low power (at zero power, to use the specialists' language), this represented a pioneer operation, although much more powerful piles were already operating in the U.S.A. and Canada.

The second stage, which was completed at the end of 1953, provided for the construction of one or two piles of medium power and a large nuclear research center.

The third stage, further off in time, would see an ap-

---

[12] He was later replaced, at his own request, by Madame Marie-Elisa Cohen, who had returned from deportation.

[13] Shortly afterward André Berthelot and Marcel Roubault were to share in the work of the committee.

proach to the problem of a big central power station (an output of 100,000 kilowatts was envisaged in Joliot's report to the Atomic Energy Committee on March 19, 1946).

If the situation was extremely favorable as regards the team at the top it was a good deal less so for the recruitment of the other echelons. The facilities granted to the C.E.A. would have made it easy for qualified people to be recruited either from the university or from private industry. But the state of the country as a whole had to be considered. This is how Joliot expressed himself on this subject:

We cannot co-opt into the C.E.A. the research workers and engineers working in laboratories and in industry whose work interests us without upsetting—in some cases very seriously—research or production which is of great importance to the country. We can only take on these men and give them work at the C.E.A. with great circumspection and often we ask them to give only a part of their time, so that they may continue their other work without too much inconvenience.

There were also many problems to be solved with regard to raw materials. Five tons of heavy water were ordered from Norway. The remaining stock of uranium from before the war had been reassembled but further supplies had to be sought in France, since the agreements made during the war between the Belgian government in exile, the U.S.A., and Britain had reserved the entire output of the Union Minère in Katanga for these two powers.[14]

A great drive to prospect for uranium and thorium both in France and her overseas territories was decided upon. But there were very few geologists available. In order to train some quickly, a School of Prospecting was set up under the direction of Professor Jean Orcel and Louis Barrabé. After this school had been in existence for four years at the Mineralogy Laboratory of the Muséum d'Histoire Naturelle, a hundred and twenty prospectors had been trained and sent out into the field. In February, 1946, the mining research team consisted of ten people. By 1947 there were already over three hundred. In 1948 very encouraging results were obtained in Haute-Vienne near La Crouzille. A new vein was discovered in addition to the one which was already being exploited in the Autun region.[15] From that time onward

---

[14] Even the Belgian physicists were entirely deprived of this metal, which had now become precious, and they had to go to Joliot to obtain a few grams of it!

[15] It is for this reason that the natural phosphate of uranium and lime is called "autunite."

France was assured of being able to produce from her own soil all the uranium she was likely to need.

"It is doubtless the first time a prospecting drive of this kind has been undertaken in France," said the High Commissioner in his report to the staff of the C.E.A. in 1947. "Many of our prospectors are young men full of drive, who fought for the Maquis during the Occupation and are glad to work in the open air."

In order to process and purify the extracted mineral a factory was built in less than a year in a great enclave in the powder mill at le Bouchet.

The prospectors first of all, and then the other divisions of the C.E.A., needed specialized electrical equipment. After the trials of four years of the Occupation French industry was not yet able to provide this. A division for making electrical equipment was therefore set up under Maurice Surdin, an extremely able engineer and a first-class organizer, and developed very quickly.

It was in 1946 that the High Commissioner, Irène Joliot-Curie, Lew Kowarski, Maurice Surdin, Léon Denivelle, and several others first entered the old fort at Châtillon which the French War Office had handed over to the C.E.A. Hundreds of tons of explosives were stored there and the previous day they had still been shooting "collaborationists" there. The work of clearing up and moving in began at once.

In July, 1946, Surdin moved in with two specialists. By April, 1947, more than twenty people were working there and detection instruments for use in prospecting were already being mass-produced. As the weeks went by new laboratories and new workshops were set up. The first experiments on the diffusion of neutrons in graphite were undertaken. The building which was to house the first French atomic pile rose from the ground. . . .

It was necessary to look ahead, to plan for the future by building a big nuclear research center. The size of this establishment would make it impossible to locate it in Paris or its immediate environs. After various sites had been explored, the plateau of Saclay was chosen, the land was bought, the plans drawn up. The overall responsibility for the building was entrusted to the great architect Auguste Perret. He was called to a meeting of the scientific committee and said:

"High Commissioner, tell me your requirements, indicate the surface areas of your buildings, and specify the limitations. I will construct a building to house your laboratories —and this building will be a palace."

"Why a palace?" asked one of the members of the committee in amazement.

"For whom can one build palaces today, if not for Science?" replied the "Master."

But unforeseen difficulties arose. The people living on the plateau were alarmed by articles in the press which were often highly fanciful and at times malicious. It was necessary to deal with the situation, not in an authoritarian manner, but by giving explanations.

Thus it was that one February evening in 1947 the little school at Saclay was the scene of unaccustomed agitation. Many cars were parked before the porch which was generally deserted at that time. In the classroom was the mayor, surrounded by most of the citizens of the commune, all of them farmers. Standing before the blackboard, Frédéric Joliot explained his plans, describing the kind of research work to be undertaken at Saclay and the safety measures which would be adopted. He also spoke of the national importance of this effort.

From time to time he would stop, examine his listeners' expressions, waiting—or asking—for questions. Soon he became aware, as did all those who had come with him, that he had won the day and that the people would trust him. That is one example, out of many one could quote, which shows Joliot's ability to establish personal contact with any kind of audience. And that night as he drove home Joliot confided to his friends that, although he was tired, he had experienced a great feeling of joy that evening—that of being able to explain himself man to man with workers who only asked in good faith to know the facts and to understand them before having to judge.

On March 8 he had to do the same thing again at the Préfecture at Versailles, and again on March 10 before the Public Health authorities. In the course of the first of these two sessions he suggested, fairly unambiguously, that some of the opposition was not due simply to the natural anxiety inspired by everything that is "atomic": "There have often been French ideas which have been exploited abroad. Look for the reasons and you will find each time either financial interests or local interests which are opposed to the development of inventions in our country."

After replying to a variety of questions he appealed to the

goodwill of the inhabitants of the region of Saclay. "You shall have it!" exclaimed the Mayor of Gif.

Today all foreign visitors of note are shown the plateau of Saclay. The "Master" Auguste Perret is no more. The palace he dreamed of has not, perhaps, been realized, but he was certainly able to give the water tower the kind of unconventional silhouette to which he attached so much importance. Frédéric Joliot is no more, but over five thousand scientists, technicians, and workmen now work where one winter in 1946, in the company of Raoul Dautry, who is also dead, and one or two other colleagues, he trod the earth of that broad plain, and as he gazed around the skyline doubtless saw in his mind's eye the chimney of the second French atomic pile, E.L.2, the sub-station, and the central workshop.

Once the nominations for the senior posts in the C.E.A. had appeared in the *Journal Officiel* on January 3, 1946, it would have been natural for this new and heavy responsibility to absorb all the energy of the High Commissioner. But the liberation of atomic energy—especially after Hiroshima and Nagasaki—posed other problems, apart from the purely scientific and technical ones.

And so in 1946 Joliot twice went to New York to take part in the work of the United Nations Atomic Energy Commission and once to London for the creation of the World Federation of Scientific Workers. When Joliot arrived in New York in June, 1946, he was at once captivated by the big city. This is how he described his impressions to the listeners of a New York radio station on July 8, 1946:

New York gives me the impression of a great ship, with all its tall skyscraper smokestacks and its many superstructures. At night life is intense. The brilliant cinema signs, the dazzling lights of the shops, and the sight of all the things we want and haven't got remind me of the Paris boulevards at Christmas when I was a child. It seems to me that it is Christmas every day in New York and that I am among grown-up children.

But New York for Joliot was more than big stores, gadgets, jazz—it was also and above all the United Nations, the diplomats, and renewed contact—after a break of seven years—with American scientists.

Frédéric Joliot-Curie, a member of the delegation, was beside Monsieur Alexandre Parodi (the leader of the delegation) when on June 25, 1946, the latter read the French Government's historic declaration, in which the following paragraph is the most noteworthy:

The atomic studies being pursued in France are character-ized by one essential trait. They are entirely directed toward peace, toward the works of peace, and toward activities the essential aim of which is the benefit of mankind.

I am authorized to say that the aims designated by the French Government for the research carried out by its scien-tists and technicians are entirely peaceful.

This line was supported by Joliot: he was indeed no strang-er to the text of this official statement. He was later on many occasions to assert that France owed it to herself to abide by it.

But although Frédéric Joliot-Curie's presence was appre-ciated by the scientists at the Atomic Energy Commission, it was much less to the taste of certain diplomats who did not care for his direct manner of speaking. In July he was recalled to Paris.

He returned to New York with his wife on September 11, 1946, however, and took an active part in the intricate discussions of the technical committee appointed by the Atomic Energy Commission. He was present when on Sep-tember 29 the Commission unanimously adopted the report presented by the Dutch scientist H. A. Kramers, which con-cluded, very diplomatically, that "control is not technically impossible."[16] Here was a source of hope and Joliot—all the participants agreed—had made a great contribution toward it. In order to show people the facts, to make governments adopt what scientists wanted, a campaign in depth on public opinion was needed. He was to devote himself to it until the time of his death with the awareness of an imperious duty to be accomplished.

This second and last visit to the U.S.A. ended in an apotheosis with a ceremony organized at Princeton on the occasion of the bicentenary of the University, and a reception at the Massachusetts Institute of Technology, Cambridge. The joy felt by the greatest atomic scientists was reflected in all their words. For Frédéric and Irène Joliot-Curie it was a resumption of contact with universal science in the happy glow of the return of peace. But a shadow hung over everything, which was to darken the atmosphere until the Geneva Conference of 1955: secrecy was still imposed on

[16] I.e., control of the implementation of a treaty banning atomic weapons.

fundamental research in nuclear physics.

Joliot had occasion to discuss this secrecy, the way it handicapped the French, and the difficulty of conditions in recently liberated France with the big American banker (big in wealth and also in stature), Bernard Baruch.

In the course of a reception he approached Joliot and with brutal and utterly American frankness he said: "So you are going back to France and with a time lag of seven years you hope to resume the development of atomic energy. Your industry will not be able to help you. You will lack the equipment you need. Your atomic pile will never see the light of day. While here . . ."

"What can you offer me here?" said Joliot with a smile.

"Laboratories, a team of colleagues and a handsome salary. At least—" [here he named a large sum].

"I should require ten times that."

"Oh! come now, you're exaggerating."

"Why? How much do you make a year yourself?"

The conversation closed without Joliot obtaining an answer. He was doubtless thinking of this illuminating exchange when he stated several months later at Versailles: "I travel a lot. It is sometimes hard to have to listen to what is said about our country. I reply that when the French become aware that a situation is particularly serious, they have always given proof of the greatest patriotism."

And he was surely thinking of it, too, at his press conference in July, 1947:[17] "We already possess enough uranium for the construction of the two experimental piles envisaged. By the end of 1948 one of the piles will certainly be completed. If the people of France so desire, we shall succeed. . . .

"That is what we have to show—it may not perhaps seem to you very much—for fourteen months of work in a country where people thought it was impossible to go in for atomic energy. It seems that abroad our will to succeed is considered an impossible folly. But our fellow scientists abroad have observed that, contrary to the prophecies, we have already passed the drawing-board stage. We have already begun to show results—modest ones, I repeat, but not negligible. If we receive help we shall succeed, without ruining the country, in giving it in a year or two's time the necessary means for the industrial and scientific development of atomic energy."

[17] Cahiers français d'information, January 15, 1948.

In the days preceding December 15, 1948, the final arrangements were made for the starting up of the first French atomic pile. The equipment was on the site. The team of people whose collaboration for the experiment would be essential was drawn up.

The reactor was to be known by the initials ZOE:[18]

"Z" for zero: the power of the pile was very small.

"O" for oxide of uranium.

"E" for "eau lourde" (heavy water).

The team reported for duty at 6.30 A.M. Everyone was at his post and, true to his custom, the High Commissioner opened the notebook in which he always wrote down his observations during the course of his experiments in the laboratory. The page for December 15 opens with the heading: *Trial start-up of ZOE*

Everyone who was gathered in the shed around this rectangular concrete block believed that everything would be all right. The calculations had been made: when the heavy water had reached a certain level, the divergent chain reaction would begin and the needles on the control panel would show this. And yet . . .

Until the experiment has been made, until we have the successful results, we are always afraid that some point may have escaped us: and at that time we were fully conscious of the great responsibilities we bore. For us, to succeed would be to settle a debt, to offer something to the nation, that is to say, to all our fellow citizens, whom we regarded as shareholders.

The first injection of heavy water was made at 7.10 A.M. After an hour and three quarters the critical level (set at 150) should have been reached and the High Commissioner wrote in his notebook: "Kowarski says it ought to begin to function."

A little later, at the level of 210:[19]

. . . then a needle on one of the dials suddenly quivered and stopped. A moment of intense emotion. We knew that something was happening. But for this phenomenon to have any value the needle would have to stop each time at a slightly higher limit. When four-fifths of the depth we had planned for was submerged in the heavy water, the slope of the general curve on the graph began to slow down: this tendency caused me several moments of anxiety. . . .

Then, as the least sensitive instruments about the hall began to react, one could see groups of assistants forming in front of

[18] The name was suggested by Lew Kowarski.
[19] Interview with Lew Kowarski in *Lettres Françaises*.

them. For twenty-five minutes we allowed it to progress continuously. I gave another good pump at about 12 minutes past 12: then the curve went shooting up. The "divergent condition" we had dreamed of had been reached. The clicking of the Geiger counters had become a continuous hum.

The members of the staff at the fort of Châtillon were certainly at their posts in their casemates converted into laboratories, but there was nevertheless an air of anxiety about that morning. So when the doors of the ZOE building opened at about 12.15 P.M. there was already a crowd waiting to hear Frédéric Joliot-Curie announcing victory.

The ovation he received on that occasion went straight to his heart, more, perhaps, than any other. It came from the team he had built up and led to its goal in the prescribed time, despite enormous difficulties. This team had just won a victory for France. When the President of the Republic, Vincent Auriol, visited ZOE six days later he referred to this team in his final words: "You are even more than a team: you are a big family working here modestly, and with admirable disinterestedness. In the name of France I thank you with all my heart."

ZOE was only a stage—the first stage. For the five years to come the High Commissioner announced at his press conference on December 16, 1948:[20] "Our task is far from being completed. In the course of the next stage, which we estimate will take five years, we must continue our activities along three principal lines of development: (1) We must operate the pile to provide the artificially radioactive elements which are needed for application in modern biology and industrial research. We must train the technicians and develop the equipment necessary for the construction of piles of medium power; (2) We must build and equip the Nuclear Research Center at Saclay, where scientists and technicians will be able to work beside new piles and big accelerators; (3) We must prospect for the mineral deposits in France and her overseas territories which will guarantee the independence of France. After that we shall see. . . ."

And he concluded: "This stage is estimated to take five years and there are grounds for believing that we can keep our promises. Provided, of course, the country has confidence in us and gives us the means to do it."

The country, certainly, had confidence. But in the face

---

[20] *Cahiers français d'information*, No. 124, January 15, 1949 p. 2.

of this success a campaign began, in France and especially abroad, which was to lead within sixteen months to the dismissal of Frédéric Joliot-Curie from his post of High Commissioner for Atomic Energy.

DISMISSAL

Throughout the year 1949 the atomic pile at Châtillon functioned continuously, apart from several interruptions for essential work and adjustments. At the end of 1949 a first bar was withdrawn from the pile and transported to the powder factory at le Bouchet where measurable quantities of plutonium were extracted from it. It was a moving moment when the group of chemists from the C.E.A. came to present the High Commissioner with this first French sample of a chemical element which did not exist on earth and which men had succeeded in manufacturing.

What a distance had been traveled since the first nuclear reaction achieved by Rutherford—since the discovery of artificial radioactivity! As Joliot turned the test tube over in his nimble fingers in order to examine it from every angle, a mental picture temporarily blotted out the object he was looking at and the group of silent colleagues: it was a picture of him and Irène presenting to Marie Curie the first chemically isolated artificially radioactive element. Then in a fraction of a second the images flashed past his mind—of the war which had kept France from being the first nation in the world to produce plutonium; of Nagasaki where on August 9, 1945, plutonium had destroyed the town in an instant, killing several tens of thousands of human beings.

But for all that the High Commissioner and his colleagues had a right to be proud that day, as on December 15, 1948. France had taken a new step forward.

While the pile continued in use at Châtillon and equipment was being built, while prospectors in France and abroad were searching for and finding uranium, work was beginning on the Nuclear Research Center at Saclay: the second pile and two accelerators were to be installed there.

Frédéric Joliot-Curie's fiftieth birthday fell on March 19, 1950, but that day he was in Stockholm. On April 6 at Montreuil his friends celebrated his birthday with a monster banquet. His closest colleagues at the C.E.A. decided to do the same thing. After some hesitations about a time and a place, they fixed it for the evening of April 26 at the "Popote des Ailes" at Viroflay.

The commissioners, directors, and heads of department were joined by the physicist Bruno Pontecorvo, formerly of the Collège de France and "one of Joliot's favourite pupils." The setting was pleasant, the food plentiful and good, the wines excellent—all things which the High Commissioner appreciated—and the atmosphere was very light hearted. But in the speech Joliot made at the end of the evening some of his remarks—which were understood by one or two of those present who were in his confidence—showed that he was seriously preoccupied about the future.

That very same afternoon Frédéric Joliot-Curie had been summoned to the office of the President of the Conseil d'Etat in the Rue de Varenne. He came into Monsieur Georges Bidault's room and heard the latter say to him: "Before taking any action against you, the administrative rules oblige me to show you your dossier. Here it is."

With a gesture the President of the Conseil indicated a cardboard folder: on the cover was the name of the High Commissioner for Atomic Energy. Inside was the decree giving his appointment. And that was all! But lying beside the dossier on the Minister's desk were a mass of newspaper clippings. . . .

The President expressed his regret at having to take such a decision. "I have already lost the friendship of Yves Farges: now I shall lose yours."

There is no doubt that Monsieur Georges Bidault's visible emotion was not feigned and that the former president of the "Conseil National de la Résistance" in dismissing from his post the famous scientist, the former president of the "Front National," was feeling the full burden of a "duty to the State" which he considered he was obliged to fulfill.

It was the declaration made by Frédéric Joliot-Curie at the congress of the French Communist Party on April 5, 1950, which furnished the pretext for his dismissal. The following passages were particularly condemned:

The imperialists wish to unleash another war against the Soviet Union and the people's democracies. . . .

In the struggle against the war of aggression which is being planned, I think of all those scientists who are serving science in the name of the people and who provide us with such a magnificent example. I think of all the new men who have already saved the world and are the hope of the world. That is why progressive scientists, Communist scientists, will never give a scrap of their science to make war against the Soviet

Union. And we will stand firm, sustained by our conviction that, by acting thus, we can serve France and the whole of mankind.

Apart from this specific declaration, Joliot's unreserved acceptance of the resolutions passed by the Gennevilliers congress of the French Communist Party was taken into account in the reasons for his dismissal.

The crisis which had thus come to a head throws a revealing light on the deep significance of the whole of Frédéric Joliot-Curie's life. His dismissal on April 29, 1950, represented the climax of a long series of pressures and demonstrations which were noticeable even before the launching of ZOE. They were considerably increased from that moment on, and they could not have failed to reach their objective while the political line followed by the real rulers of France remained unchanged.

As early as 1947 in certain industrial and financial circles there was a curious reserve with regard to the C.E.A. "We have our eye on you, we are watching to see how you get on," was the reply received one day from a leading personality in industry, when he was approached about the recruitment of specialist personnel. As the C.E.A. developed, so did the number increase of those who were astonished to see at its head a scientist who was also an engineer, who was not a member of that great family of former pupils of the École Polytechnique and who, worst of all, permitted himself to be a Communist.

On March 18, 1948, when the preparations for the trial of the first French atomic pile were going well, a first and violent objection was made at the Conseil de la République. But the ground was not yet prepared and the Conseil de la République gave the High Commissioner a favorable vote (83 to 79), though with a considerable number of abstentions. The same day, March 17, by a curious coincidence, Irène Joliot-Curie, although she carried a visa for the U.S., was refused entry to New York and was detained for several days on Ellis Island, along with the prohibited immigrants, before finally being admitted after widespread protests.

The successful starting of ZOE unleashed a veritable storm of articles and from that moment onward the pressure was hardly relaxed. The tone was set by *Time* magazine, which carried the headline: A COMMUNIST PILE. *The Economist* said on December 25, 1948:

. . .There is some alarm in the United States at the prospect of a French development in this field with key scientific positions being held by Communists. . . . Atomic research in France with Communist participation is hardly compatible in the long run with French military commitments in the Western or Atlantic Union. . . .

And the New York *Herald Tribune* (European edition for December 27, 1948, an article signed by Stephen White):

The existence of the French pile is a veritable threat to the measures which the English-speaking nations have seen fit to adopt. Many people consider the threat to be aggravated by the fact that the director of the French operations, Doctor Frédéric Joliot-Curie, is an avowed communist.

And one could go on with quotations of this kind. The general observation, which was made with some bitterness, was that the Anglo-American monopoly of atomic energy within what is called "the West" had to come to an end.

As for the fears which were voiced about atomic secrets, they were completely without foundation. The C.E.A. was a civil establishment, solely devoted to technical and industrial scientific research. With regard to secrecy in matters of fundamental scientific research, Joliot's position had always been firm and unchanging. He had had occasion to reaffirm it in 1939 in reply to Léo Szilard.

As for "technical or industrial secrets," his position was equally clear and indeed obvious. However, faced with the fuss provoked by the success of ZOE, he was anxious to make matters quite clear and he took the opportunity at a lunch given him by the Anglo-American press on January 5, 1949, to do so:

First of all, the results of fundamental research which we obtain in this field will continue to be published, and thus all the countries in the world, including the U.S.S.R., will be able to profit from them.

As regards the results of practical research, which we obtain, needless to say, with a view to their peaceful application, but which could have military uses, it seems to me necessary to keep them secret until weapons of mass destruction, like the atomic bomb, have been outlawed by the United Nations Organization.

A French Communist, like any other French citizen who occupies a post which has been entrusted to him by the government, cannot possibly in good faith consider communicating, to any foreign power whatever, results which are not his own property but which belong to the collective body which permits him to work. Any Communist is perfectly well aware of the necessity for this conduct.

Let us be frank. If I or one of my colleagues tomorrow made a discovery which was essential to the production of atomic weapons, the authors of the articles I have quoted believe that it would be our duty—voluntarily accepted—to communicate all the details to the Moscow government. It therefore seems that we are committing the crime of treason "by intention" and that we should be punished in advance. What is the factual basis for this accusation? Or, in the absence of facts, what premises could there be for this absurd reasoning, which makes people believe that being a Communist absolves one morally from French nationality and automatically transforms one into a paid or unpaid spy?

Certainly Communists, and not only Communists, have a great admiration for the achievements of the Soviet Union, just as many people at the time looked with hope to revolutionary France in 1792.

Were not republicans, who struggled against social injustice and the monarchy in their own countries, already then regarded as "French agents"? And yet they were pure and authentic patriots. Like republicans today, like all progressive elements, we wish to campaign in our own country, within the framework of our democratic constitution, for the establishment of more social justice and more prosperity, conditions which we consider to be favorable to the peaceful organization of a socialist world.

Three and a half months later he took a stand once more on the possibility of France making an atomic bomb. On April 23, 1949, at the National Conference of the "Mouvement des Intellectuels Français" he said:

I believe that in order to defend the peace by peaceful and effective means, we must translate our will into actions, into commitments which will require courage. It is not enough to say: I am for peace. That is easy! It compromises nobody. Everyone agrees with you.

But here, on the other hand, is a definite and effective commitment which we can make and must make: if in our professions we are asked—as has happened to me in my own field—if tomorrow we are asked to work for war, to work on the atomic bomb, we must reply: No![21]

[21] It is interesting to compare these words with the view given by P. M. S. Blackett on the subject of Joliot's dismissal (*Biographical Memoir:* p. 100): "This took place not only at a time of great political tension resulting from the Korean War, but at a period when the French Government changed the original object of the French atomic organization, which initially was to be concerned with industrial and scientific aspects of atomic energy, and decided to make atomic bombs."

This is a commitment and we will stand by it. It may certainly have awkward consequences. Some people may lose in personal status. For others it may be even more serious. We have seen this in the United States, where men have lost their jobs. Well, then! We must help them. That is also something we can do. Those who have not yet been forced to take a stand must help those who have taken it and who may be suffering the bitter consequences.

A frontal attack having failed, attempts were made to reduce the credits granted to the C.E.A.—not without letting it be understood that with a different man in charge the position might be reconsidered. But there were swift and vigorous reactions to this. The Académie des Sciences, in particular, met in secret committee on April 11, 1949, and unanimously adopted an extremely firmly worded resolution which was sent to the government.

Frédéric Joliot-Curie's visit to the U.S.S.R. in November, 1949, and his lecture to the Academy of Sciences there on the anniversary of ZOE gave a fresh pretext for attacks, the sense of which was made clear by a declaration of the President of the United States, according to which, "The United States Government will seek in the near future to gain control of the production of uranium in all parts of the world outside the Soviet sphere of influence."

Even a rapid survey of these facts and texts shows clearly that the declaration made at Gennevilliers—which, in any case, in condemning a possible war of aggression conformed to the letter and spirit of the Constitution of the French Republic—was simply used as a pretext for eliminating Frédéric Joliot-Curie from his post as director, in which technically and objectively he had succeeded, while committing the great crime of expressing unorthodox views on problems of a general nature. The Catholic writer Louis-Martin Chauffier summed up the situation very well at the time: "Joliot had too much science and too much conscience. He worked too well and refused to yield. He has been driven out; that is in the established order of things."

As for Frédéric Joliot-Curie's immediate colleagues, Francis Perrin (the Commissioner), Lew Kowarski, B. Goldschmidt, J. Guéron (directors), and nine heads of departments affirmed on April 28, 1950: "Contrary to the opinion which is unfortunately widespread, the C.E.A. is not a national defense establishment and we are of the opinion that the post of High Commissioner does not imply any restrictions on the holder's right of self-expression."

Thus it was basically the "Communist" they decided to strike down. It was not possible in the eyes of the rulers of France to let it be shown by experience that a man holding these views could succeed at his task and serve his country effectively. In addition to this, it is logical to assume that the desire to offer something to the Americans, in the hope—which remained unfulfilled—of deriving some "atomic secrets" from them in return, also played its part in the decision.

During the years that followed his dismissal, many vexations were inflicted on Frédéric and Irène Joliot-Curie.

In 1955, under the pressure of public opinion, an undoubted détente occurred in international relations. It was the scientists, many of whom had struggled for this since 1946, who were the first to benefit in a spectacular manner. At Geneva, in July, 1955, the "atomic scientists" of all nations met together. Americans, Russians, Englishmen, Frenchmen, Indians, and others discussed subjects that had hitherto been kept taboo. The delegation formed by the French Government was large and the exhibition they presented was a great success. But, to the general astonishment, the discoverers of artificial radioactivity, of the fission of uranium, and of the chain reaction were not included in the delegation. At Monsieur Francis Perrin's press conference a foreign journalist expressed surprise at the absence of the two French scientists who had been awarded the Nobel Prize for nuclear chemistry. The reply could only be an embarrassed one: "The French Government did not consider their participation to be necessary."

The French Government went further: the names of Frédéric and Irène Joliot-Curie were nowhere mentioned on the panels of the French exhibition—although they were given prominence on those of the British exhibit. Several countries had expressed a wish for Joliot to be invited to give one of the big public lectures in the evening. The French delegation decided not to take up this offer. And yet those who were responsible for these decisions knew that they could not succeed in effacing history.

The university men, on the other hand, had insisted, a year before, on arranging a brilliant celebration at the Sorbonne for the twentieth anniversary of the discovery of artificial radioactivity.

Added to all this there were the small personal rebuffs:

colleagues who cut him, eyes that avoided his, handshakes that were withheld, acquaintances who broke off contact or became distant. Other men, less sensitive than Joliot, would have suffered less. All those who knew him in those years can testify to his sadness and bitterness. One of his pupils, Pierre Radvanyi, writes:[22] "At one stage Joliot was able to say that the number of people who came and shook his hand and spoke to him in the course of the meetings he attended served him as a very accurate barometer of the international situation."

There were, of course, the messages of sympathy from pupils and friends, known and unknown, which arrived in thousands from places in France and abroad. There were many and widespread demonstrations of protest. On May 5, 1950, at 11. A.M. he gave his usual lecture at the Collège de France in a lecture room that was absolutely packed. The long bench intended for apparatus was buried that day under bouquets of flowers. After the entire group in the lecture room had risen to its feet as a man and sung the "Marseillaise" the ex-High Commissioner for Atomic Energy, his voice choked with emotion, announced that he was going to discuss the nuclear reactions caused by charged particles. He did, however, permit himself a few brief introductory remarks. After referring to certain disturbances which had occurred at the top of the C.E.A., he uttered a cry of warning to his listeners on the subject of the terribly insufficient importance granted to science:

Science is indispensable to this country. A power can only justify its independence by the original contributions it makes to other nations. If it does not do this it will be colonized. It is for the sake of patriotism that the scientist must develop and enlighten his fellow citizens about the role of science—which should liberate man, not serve to increase private profit. If the scientist has not a certain courage, how can he justify his presence in the laboratory? That is politics, you may say. But politics is a fine thing, which people seek to discredit for bad reasons.

[22] *La Pensée,* No. 87, 1959, p. 84.

6

Defending Science and Peace

As a result of his general thought, the nature of his own research work, the conversations he had with Madame Curie, Paul Langevin, and other colleagues, Joliot was particularly sensitive to all matters concerning the uses to which discoveries and inventions were put. The spring and summer of 1945 witnessed a sequence of events which forced the conscience of all mankind—but more particularly that of all scientists—to confront the whole question of the social implications of science. On May 8, 1945, the war in Europe came to an end. It continued in Asia, but the outcome was no longer in doubt. It was then that the terrible weapon made its appearance. On August 6, 1945, at 8.15 A.M., the superfortress *Enola Gay* dropped an atomic device on the Japanese town of Hiroshima. A few kilograms of uranium 235 destroyed a hundred thousand people. On August 9, 1945, the airplane *Grand Artiste* dropped a plutonium bomb on the port of Nagasaki. There were seventy thousand victims. . . .

The atomic age opened for mankind under these terrible auspices. Few men at that time could conceive of the nature of the atomic bomb and estimate the repercussions of its use in war. Some scientists, like the German physicist W. Heisenberg, refused for several days to believe that there had been a liberation of the energy stored in the atomic nuclei. But they soon had to accept the evidence. As for Joliot, his personal contribution to the fundamental discoveries about fission—as well as the fragments of information which had reached him—made it impossible for him to doubt it for a moment.

On August 10, 1945, the day after the bombing of Nagasaki, he wrote a detailed article which was published in the newspaper *L'Humanité* on August 12, 1945.

It is also true that the immense reserves of energy contained in the uranium devices can be liberated slowly enough to be used practically for the benefit of mankind. I am personally convinced that, despite the feelings aroused by the application of atomic energy to destructive ends, it will be of inestimable service to mankind in peacetime.

After going over the history of atomic research, he concluded:

The achievements both of research and of invention in the United States must command our admiration, but it is nonetheless true that it was in France that the first working principles were discovered: these constitute a contribution of the first importance to this new conquest of nature by man.

The war ended in Asia as well. But the feelings of relief and hope were gradually replaced by uneasiness and alarm about what had been accomplished. It was natural for scientists to be the first to realize the immensity of the threat —and that is what happened. Only the Americans at that time were informed. They were the first to react—and they did so in an admirable manner. On June 11, 1945, more than a month before the Alamogordo test,[1] a report drawn up by a committee of seven American scientists presided over by Professor James Franck was sent to Mr. Stimson, the United States Secretary of War.[2] This report, which was of the greatest importance, came out categorically against any future use of the atomic bomb in the war against Japan.

It may be very difficult to persuade the world that a nation which was capable of secretly preparing and suddenly using a new weapon as indiscriminate as the rocket bomb and a thousand times more destructive, is to be trusted in its proclaimed desire of having such weapons abolished by international agreement.

Having proposed a public demonstration on a desert island the report concluded:

We believe that these considerations make the use of nuclear bombs for an early attack against Japan inadvisable. If the United States were to be the first to use this new means of indiscriminate destruction of mankind, she would sacrifice public support throughout the world, precipitate the

[1] It was at Alamogordo in the New Mexico desert that the first atomic bomb was tested on July 15, 1945.

[2] The report was published in May, 1946, by *The Chicago Bulletin of Atomic Scientists*. The signatories, apart from J. Franck, were L. Szilard, E. Rabinovitch, D. Hughes, T. Hogness, G. Seaborg, and C. J. Niekson.

race for armaments and prejudice the possibility of reaching an international agreement on the future control of such weapons.

Sixty-four other American scientists addressed a petition to President Truman on the same lines.

As the documents concerning the period immediately before the bombing of Hiroshima and Nagasaki became public, the significance of the United States decision to use atomic weapons became clearer and more alarming for the future. The reasons for this decision were not military, but diplomatic. At the end of an exhaustive analysis of all the available documents, the British physicist and Nobel Prize winner P. M. S. Blackett was forced to conclude:[3]

As far as our analysis has taken us we have found no compelling military reason for the clearly very hurried decision to drop the first atomic bomb on 6 August. But a most compelling diplomatic reason, relating to the balance of power in the postwar world, is clearly discernible. . . .

So, in truth, we conclude that the dropping of the atomic bombs was not so much the last military act of the Second World War as the first act of the cold diplomatic war with Russia now in progress.

In Europe and then throughout the world, scientists were not slow to draw conclusions from this collection of facts and circumstances.

After the liberation of Paris, Joliot several times had occasion to visit London. Before the exploding of the first atomic bomb he also received an invitation for Irène and himself to go to the United States. An American military aircraft picked them up in Paris and took them first to London, where they had to wait several days before being told that their visit was canceled. The same military aircraft took them back to Paris and on the return journey the crew were a good deal less polite. They later found out that the security forces had been afraid the two French scientists might ask to see American colleagues who were engaged in atomic research, in which case it would have been impossible to explain the true reason why they could not be contacted.

In London Joliot had been delighted to meet again a group of French scientists gathered around the remarkable leader Louis Rapkine. They had managed, thanks to Rapkine, to escape from France during the course of the war and to reach Britain, Canada, and the United States. He also met several members of a Franco-British group of scientists set

[3] P. M. S. Blackett, *Military and Political Consequences of Atomic Energy,* London, 1948, pp. 123 and 127.

up before 1939 with a view to developing scientific cooperation between the two countries. It was in this group that he had already met Lord Suffolk, long before their encounter in Bordeaux.[4]

He also had conversations with certain members of the British Association of Scientific Workers, which in February, 1946, organized a conference on the theme: "Science and the Welfare of Mankind." Scientists from nine different countries were present and it was in the course of these discussions that the idea of creating an international organization of scientists was born. The British Association was asked to prepare a draft constitution and on July 20 and 21, 1946, the assembly was held which ended with the creation, amid general enthusiasm, of the World Federation of Scientific Workers.

Three days later, still in London, the executive council of the new Federation met and chose as its president Frédéric Joliot-Curie.[5] Joliot later recalled this period, which was to lead him to embark on a long-term campaign with regard to his colleagues all over the world, in a message he sent to the Federation at the celebration of its tenth anniversary in Peking[6] in 1956.

When the founders of this world organization of scientific workers first met together in 1946 humanity had only just emerged from a terrible nightmare. . . .

During the very last stages of this terrible conflict the atomic bomb appeared. Its destructive power and the real reasons for its use at Hiroshima and Nagasaki—contrary to the far-sighted advice of many of our American colleagues—immediately faced mankind with new problems at the very moment when everything should have united men in a common desire to rebuild and to draw closer together.

All the delegates at the inaugural conference in London, as at the first executive council in Paris, and all the scientists who were represented by these delegates, had the strong feeling that, even more than in the past, the rapid development

[4] The British members of the group included Bernal, Blackett, and Zuckerman.

[5] He continued to exercise the office of President with authority and dedication until 1957; it was the British scientist C. F. Powell, also a Nobel Prize winner, who succeeded him.

[6] Joliot always dreamed of going to China. He was several times invited, but was unfortunately never able to go. But during the course of an executive council meeting in Vienna in 1952 he did have the pleasure of meeting again his pupil Tsien San-tsiang.

of science and its applications would pose difficult problems —about which it was impossible for scientists who were conscious of their responsibilities to keep silent.

He himself could not have been further from the thought of evading these responsibilities which he had sought out for himself. He felt himself more directly concerned than others with the problems which faced mankind as a result of the existence of atomic weapons, because his own research had contributed directly to these problems. It was equally natural for him to wonder one day how those whom he considered his masters would have acted in the same situation. On November 7, 1947, in the course of the ceremony organized by the World Federation of Scientific Workers on the tenth anniversary of Lord Rutherford's death, Joliot spoke these words:

What would Rutherford's position have been, if he had been faced with the problems posed by the existence of the atomic bomb? It is difficult to say.

At all events at New Islington Public Hall on February 7, 1916, during the First World War, Rutherford was replying to questions put to him by engineers about the liberation of the energy of radium for useful purposes, and said: "If we could liberate the energy of a pound of this substance at a suitable rate, this would correspond to the use of 100 million pounds of coal." He added: "Fortunately we have not at present discovered the method of doing this and I personally hope it is not discovered until men are living at peace with one another."

Now the method had been discovered, in time of war and for military purposes. It had not only been discovered but put into operation for lethal ends. But Joliot, in his speech, refused to give up hope and continued:

The fears which now grip us must give way to a great and firm hope, which is based on the objective consideration of the feats achieved by science and to a revelation of the beneficial prospects it offers us. Thanks to men of science like Ernest Rutherford, our horizon is illumined by a destiny more inspiring than any of those so far predicted and the scientist continues his work with confidence. . . .

Joliot took an active part in the composition of the documents for the constitution of the World Federation of Scientific Workers. Among these documents special mention must be given to the *Scientific Workers' Charter,* of which the principal author was the great British scientist J. D. Bernal, on whom Paul Langevin had once bestowed the title of "world citizen."

Twelve years of fighting side by side established a deep friendship and mutual regard between Joliot and Bernal. Bernal once gave the following description of Joliot's campaign with regard to scientists:

There remained for him another task to be performed, a more difficult one and one about which less is known— that of rallying almost the whole scientific world against atomic warfare. It was not a question here of uniting people who could agree on the main political issues, but rather of bringing in people of different disciplines and interests to realize that the problem of avoiding nuclear war was more important than all the others.

In 1947 Joliot wrote an "Introduction" for the World Federation of Scientific Workers in which he explained the reasons why action by scientists on a world scale seemed to him essential.

A generation ago no one seriously doubted that science, a manifestation of the highest qualities of the human spirit, was the richest source of material and intellectual benefits. Of course the spread of scientific knowledge has always encountered powerful enemies among those who hold to mystical imperatives and those whose profits and privileges require the people over whom they hold sway to be in a state of fear and ignorance. But despite the early difficulties and injustices caused by the abuse of scientific discoveries, the people's faith in science continued to grow.

But the events of the last decades and the arrival of the atomic bomb ran the risk of reversing this current of opinion.

It seems to me that before passing judgment, a distinction must be made between pure scientific knowledge and the uses to which it is put, to distinguish—in brief—between science in thought and in action.

Pure scientific knowledge brings peace to our minds—and a firm confidence in the ascendancy of man—by banishing superstitions and the fear of invisible forces and by giving us an increasingly clear understanding of our situation in the universe. *It is, furthermore, and this is one of its highest merits, a fundamental factor for unity between the minds of men all over the globe.*[7]

After once again denouncing the ill effects of secrecy with regard to fundamental research, he returns to the moral value of science.

[7] Joliot's italics.

Science is sometimes considered to be in itself moral or immoral according to the uses that are made of it. Most discoveries and inventions have a double aspect, beneficial as well as destructive. It is the men who make use of them who must alone be judged. It is unnecessary to refer here to the most notorious misuses of science, what one may call the perversions of science. There is no denying that the difficulties of our age are, to a great extent, a consequence of them. But one may equally be justified in believing that we should be subject to even more tragic difficulties—and in what a powerless state—if science had not progressed. Many scientists rightly believe that the perversions of science can be avoided. They do not wish to be the accomplices of those people who are permitted by a bad social organization to exploit the results of their work for harmful or selfish ends. There can be no denying that the scientific world is undergoing a crisis of conscience and that the scientist's sense of social responsibility grows greater and better defined every day. Scientists and technicians do not and cannot belong to an élite which is detached from practical contingencies. As citizen members of the great community of workers, they must necessarily be concerned with the use society makes of their discoveries and inventions in order to insure that science is used to the full for peace and for the benefit of mankind.

Meanwhile the anxiety caused by the extension of the cold war and the spread of knowledge about the dangers of an atomic war were to lead to the formations of groups and movements in many places. The founders and leaders of these movements turned to the leader already chosen by the scientists and asked him to lead them. It was thus that Frédéric Joliot-Curie came to be at the head of the crusade for peace.

On February 24, 1948, thirty people, workers and intellectuals—most of them former members of the Resistance—met together in a room at the highly respectable Hôtel des Deux-Mondes in the Avenue de l'Opéra, Paris. The movement known as the "Combattants de la Liberté" (Fighters for Liberty) had recently been founded under the presidency of Yves Farge. This was to become the "Combattants de la Liberté et de la Paix" and then the "Mouvement de la Paix" (Peace Movement). Joliot was present at this assembly.

In April, 1948, the congress organized by the "Liaison Committee of Intellectuals" met at Wroclaw in Poland. Joliot was unable to go but Irène Joliot-Curie was in the French delegation, along with Madame Eugénie Cotton, Pablo Picasso, the Abbé Boulier, and de Vercors.

In December, 1948, the Bureau of the "Women's International Democratic Federation" met in Budapest and they, like the "Liaison Committee of Intellectuals," expressed the desire to see a big international peace congress meeting as soon as possible. Madame Eugénie Cotton was instructed to ask Joliot if he would act as president of this Congress.

He did not give me his final reply right away. First he expressed the view that since women had played the decisive role in the struggle for liberation during the Second World War, it would be appropriate to elect a woman as president and not a man. I was extremely gratified by Frédéric Joliot-Curie's appreciation of the part played by women but I still insisted that he himself should become the president of the International Congress which was to take place at the Salle Pleyel, Paris, in April, 1949. He gave his acceptance a few days later and it was very fortunate for the Peace Movement that he did.[8]

On February 25, 1949, a preparatory committee launched the appeal for the convocation of the Pleyel Congress. This took place in a clean bare office at 2 Rue de l'Elysée, Paris, where six people were gathered around a trestle table. These six people must have been greatly struck at that moment by the importance of Joliot's gesture, for one of them, Professor J. D. Bernal, was to refer to it in August, 1958, when speaking to the huge crowd which accompanied the scientist to his last resting place.

When he accepted the presidency of the Congress, Joliot knew that the task would be burdensome and time-consuming. He knew it would call for uninterrupted work over many years, work that would be added to that which he had already undertaken on behalf of other organizations. He knew, in addition, that he must preserve the relative independence of different organizations which, although they had the same president, operated in different fields. But he did not think he could avoid his duty and from that moment onward he was to devote an important part of his days to the campaign for peace.

On the morning of April 20, 1949, the neighborhood of the Salle Pleyel, in the Rue du Faubourg Saint-Honoré, Paris, was the scene of unaccustomed activity. On the pavement outside and in the vast hall which gives access to the various concert halls, one could hear the languages, see the costumes, and meet the people of every continent. In spite of the dif-

---

[8] *La Pensée,* No. 87, September-October, 1959, p. 66.

ferences in their appearances, they had one thing in common: the expressions of joy and determination on their faces and in their eyes. The "Partisans of Peace" were to hold their first Congress.[9]

Let us enter the big hall, which is filled with the din that always precedes the opening of these assemblies. Standing up behind the battery of microphones, the writer Jean Lafitte calls on the members of the presidium to take their places on the platform. A few minutes go by. A relative quiet comes over the hall. At the center of the long table Frédéric Joliot-Curie gets up, draws from his pocket a sheaf of notes, adjusts his glasses, arranges the microphone. . . .

I declare the World Congress of the Partisans of Peace to be open.[10]

He then has to wait several minutes before he can continue. The delegates from seventy-two countries rise to their feet and acclaim the great scientist. All, whether they come from Europe, Asia, Africa, America, or Australia; whether they live in socialist or capitalist countries; whether their own nations are powerful or small, independent or subject, all realize the value of this symbol: the first work of the Congress which, at the dawn of the atomic era, is to undertake to safeguard the peace of the world, is to be presided over by one of the scientists who had done the most to enable man to liberate the energy locked up in the heart of matter. All are happy, all are proud, and the French (let us admit) a little more so than the others—for it is one of their countrymen speaking in their capital and in their language who is the first to address the world.

Frédéric Joliot-Curie can finally continue. He greets the delegates and makes special mention of those from "democratic China, republican Spain, democratic Greece, Vietnam, and the Indonesian Republic." He retraces the history of the Congress, analyzes the situation. When he seeks to explain the particular reasons which scientists had for defending the peace, his train of thought inevitably leads him to refer to his master:

It is not necessary to remind you of all that civilization

[9] It should be remembered that on the same day in Prague there was a meeting of all those who had been refused an entry visa to France.

[10] The text of Frédéric Joliot-Curie's opening report is given on page 171).

owes to scientific research, of all the great changes in the living conditions and the ideas of men which it has brought about. As Paul Langevin was fond of saying, science makes possible the material emancipation of man, which is the necessary condition for his moral and intellectual emancipation.

And he ends his report—to a standing ovation from the delegates: .

We appeal to all people of goodwill to avoid this scourge of war. Together and conscious of our strength, we will fight this struggle in the confidence of victory.

The Pleyel Congress ended in the apotheosis of the rally at the Buffalo Stadium. There again, speaking before the immense and attentive crowd, in which young people were visibly in the majority, Frédéric Joliot-Curie invited all the popular forces to mobilize for the preservation of the threatened peace.

Then he began his long tour of the capitals. On may 17, 1949, he went to London once more. Five meetings were held simultaneously and the speakers were taken from one meeting to the next around the clock in a system of relays. As midnight drew near, they all met in the small sitting room of the scientific writer J. G. Crowther, which scarcely contained the great voice of Paul Robeson, who with J. D. Bernal had taken part in these meetings "in rotation."

Paris in April, London in May, Rome in October, 1949.

In the report he presented in the latter city at the opening of the session of the Committee of the World Congress of the Partisans of Peace, he spoke of the reasons which had induced him to involve himself fully in the struggle for peace. Before 1914, as before 1939, courageous men had already joined together in many countries to try to prevent the drift to war. Joliot believed they had been unsuccessful because their appeals had not been addressed to all men, whatever their occupation, social position, or nationality. It had not been possible then—but it must be possible now—to convince all mankind that this problem of war and peace is not dependent on mysterious and inaccessible forces, any more than that it is the predestined fate of our species. This problem depends on the peoples of the world and they must grasp this fact. He had already made this point in his report to the Pleyel Congress:

Every one of the millions of people who make up the nations threatened by war must convince himself that the problem of war and peace is one which is personal to him, which concerns him directly, and which it is impossible for him to evade. He should not feel powerless, because at the same time all over the world millions of people like him are asking the same questions: they are going to take action for peace and add their efforts to his own.

In Rome he concluded:

In Paris last April we laid the foundations of a vast peace movement, a prolonged campaign to denounce and put to rout the warmongers. . . .
Tomorrow we shall meet somewhere else, still inspired by the same faith, still resolved to try every means in our power to save our children from knowing the horrors of a new war, to prevent science being criminally deflected from its true purpose and to ensure that the accumulated efforts of all the workers of the world produce happiness and not ruin. We will continue in this way until the danger has been removed. Nothing will stop us.

In 1950 this struggle for life, this defense of peace, was to receive a decisive impulse at the end of the meeting of the Committee of the World Congress at Stockholm.

In his report Joliot first of all put the accent on an idea—and one can only wonder today how certain people at that time could have described it as revolutionary, illusory, or hypocritical—that of "coexistence."

The United Nations Organization ceases to exist if confidence is lost. In the present state of international relations the re-establishing of confidence seems to me to be dependent on the essential belief that coexistence and cooperation between capitalist and socialist countries is possible and desirable.
This principle seems to us to conform to historical truth and in order to accept it we have only to examine it honestly without worrying in the first place about who formulated it.

Then he tackled the problems of atomic energy. He could not fail to recall the closing words of the lecture he had delivered in that same city on December 12, 1935 (see page 12). What had been bold prophecies at that time had now become menacing reality.

I must admit that I had in mind a more distant date. Less than fifteen years' work has sufficed for scientists to achieve this prodigious application of our knowledge.
If I were here to make a survey of what has been achieved in this field during these fifteen-odd years and to look ahead to the possibilities which lie before us, I should have to tell

of magnificent experiments and horrible destruction.

The fact that the admirable series of scientific discoveries, begun at the dawn of the twentieth century by Henri Becquerel and Pierre and Marie Curie, should have ended with the human race being threatened by destruction from the hydrogen bomb constitutes a serious warning to us all and above all to scientists.

After five days of concentrated discussion the delegates decided to address a solemn appeal to the world. The text of this appeal would be submitted individually to all, so that those who approved of the text should sign it.

On March 19, 1950, on his fiftieth birthday, Joliot was given a white sheet of paper on which were typed the four paragraphs of the text, which has become a part of history as the "Stockholm Appeal."

We demand the absolute banning of atomic weapons which are weapons of terror and of the mass destruction of whole populations.

We demand the setting up of rigorous international control to guarantee the implementation of this ban.

We consider that a government which is the first to use atomic weapons against any other country is committing a crime against humanity and should be regarded as war criminals.

We call upon all men of goodwill in the world to sign this appeal.

Eight months later, when he presented the opening report to the Second World Congress of the Partisans of Peace in Warsaw, five hundred million signatures had already been collected.

I should like to say here and now that it will never be possible to pay a sufficient tribute to the men and women of goodwill all over the world who have gone individually to seek out their fellow citizens, in order to talk to them about these problems, to correct their mistaken beliefs, and to take note of their suggestions. . . .

This great international consultation of the people has caused those who have taken part in it to examine problems which they had sometimes never thought about before. It has caused them to study the effectiveness of the measures proposed and to ask themselves whether these measures, though necessary, were sufficient.

It was not at Warsaw but at Sheffield that this second Congress of the Partisans of Peace was to have been held. The mayor of this city was willing, but the British Government decided differently. Joliot was not allowed to land on British soil and was sent back like a prohibited immigrant.

He spent the return trip in the cabin of the captain, who was indignant at the treatment the French scientist had received. On their arrival at Dunkirk, Joliot was greeted by a demonstration, organized by the dockers several minutes before, and presented with a huge bouquet of flowers. An hour later the Dunkirk telephone exchange received a call from Prague for Professor Joliot-Curie "somewhere in Dunkirk." The telephone operators were only too delighted systematically to ring up every place where he might be. They discovered the café where the "pilgrims of peace" were taking refreshment and connected the physicist Joliot-Curie with the writer Ilya Ehrenburg. It was decided to hold the Congress in Warsaw.

Within a few days the Poles achieved the tour de force of organizing the reception—and facilities for a meeting—of two thousand and sixty-five delegates from eighty countries. At the end of this Congress it was decided to create a new organization, the World Peace Council. Joliot was appointed president of it by acclamation.

Among those who heard Joliot speak in Warsaw was the great Polish physicist Leopold Infeld. This was the first of many meetings between them. He writes: [11]

How well I remember Frédéric Joliot-Curie's first speech to the Congress! There was not the slightest trace in it of facile rhetoric. His exposition was serious and objective yet eloquent and persuasive. During those unforgettable days of the Warsaw Congress there were numerous occasions on which I met Professor Joliot-Curie. . . .

I was always conscious of the air of greatness which emanated from this man. This quality was only emphasized by his modesty and his friendly and kindly manner. I remember we discussed Marxism and spoke of the need to interpret it without dogmatism. We also discussed the dangers of dogmatism in scientific thought.

After Warsaw, Helsinki. After Helsinki, Vienna. After Vienna, Paris. Then Vienna again, Prague, Budapest, and so on. Sometimes it would be for working meetings of small committees, sometimes for a big congress. In order to prepare for them he had to build up and refer to a large library of documents, receive visitors, seek audiences, write, talk, reply to letters. . . . Joliot devoted himself to all these tasks with a sense of his responsibilities as the president of an immense movement which was struggling to preserve

[11] *La Pensée*, No. 87, September-October, 1959, p. 52.

something inestimably precious: peace between men.

For all the people who took part in those Congress sessions the memory of Frédéric Joliot-Curie will remain associated with a whole series of images, which together go to make up the characteristic atmosphere of those occasions.

Whatever the meeting place might be (hall, theater, concert hall) certain functional elements are always present: the flags, the banners covered with slogans, the piles of headphones which give translations in various languages, the long tables on which duplicated texts are stacked up, the technical equipment.

Not far from the hall where the meetings are held there is an office with the door labeled "President." Before the Congress, and as it proceeds, Joliot sees many people there day and night. These interviews are a continuation of those which take place in his house at Antony or in his study at the Collège de France. They represent an unobtrusive but extremely important part of his work for peace. It can be summed up in one quip better than in many long sentences: one day when he had been talking to Joliot in his office, between two sessions of a Congress, Yves Farge remarked to a friend he met in the corridor: "I've just been to confession."

The differences between the people which throng the meeting hall and the corridors are not only those of language, skin color, and costume. Everyone comes to the Congress with his own vision of international problems. The emphasis given by each one to a certain danger or incident is different, according to whether they come from Norway or Bolivia, from Great Britain or the Cameroons, from the Soviet Union or Ceylon. And it is one of the President's most difficult tasks to know how to make allowances for all these factors.

When the Congress hall is full and the meeting has been declared open, a relative silence descends and the President of the World Peace Council, dressed in a dark suit, his features drawn with fatigue, a few sheets of paper in his hand, advances toward the rostrum and the microphones. The people on the platform and in the hall rise to their feet and applaud. Hundreds of pairs of eyes are turned on this man of medium stature who appears a fairly slight figure. They look at him with emotion and with gratitude.

As for Frédéric Joliot-Curie, he always feels at this precise moment an emotion that is never dulled by repetition. His extraordinary sensibility enables him to make personal con-

tact with every one of the people who have come to attend
the Congress, some of them from the antipodes. His wear-
iness disappears and he begins the first sentences of his
report in a clear and ringing voice.

One by one he reads the pages of his notes: sometimes
he departs from them, comments as he goes along, impro-
vises. He interrupts himself to take a drink of water and
continues in a dramatic or passionate tone—sometimes even
a violent one. But the qualities of the scientist are always
reflected in what he says: precise use of words and rigorous
analysis of ideas.

Sometimes before the session, Joliot-Curie, clad in the
black-and-white-check jacket he wears at home, will be sitting
at his desk in his house at Antony. To his right he can cast
envious glances through the french windows at the tennis
coure, where his son, Pierre, is playing a game with Irène or
one of his friends. Behind him is a panel covered with an
artistically arranged jumble of photographs: his wife, his
children, Langevin, Lenin, a meeting hall, his colleagues by
the atomic pile at Châtillon, the scene of the demonstration
at Oradour-sur-Glane, a picture taken in a cloud chamber. . . .

In front of him are several pages covered with notes.
But it is obvious that these sheets of paper have only just
taken the place of the *Physical Review* which is still open
and has been pushed aside to his left against his slide rule
and an ashtray—the contents of which are eloquent.

In a tray to his right there are newspapers, brochures,
pamphlets; another tray contains letters; a third, scientific
periodicals in English and Russian. . . . And opposite him
one or two close colleagues have taken their places, with
blank paper and pens in hand. In the dining room behind
him a secretary is waiting, or is already making a fair copy
of a text.

"I have sketched out the main points in my report. Look—"

And the discussion begins. He is determined that no points
shall remain obscure. He is eager for their comments on all
the allusions in it. He invites the others to act as "devil's
advocate."

Irène comes in to announce that the meal is ready. She
gets a very poor reception: "You have an absolute genius
for interrupting a discussion just when everything is about
to become clear!"

She vanishes—but returns obstinately every ten minutes,
until in the end he admits defeat with a smile. And so on

for two or three days. Each time will come the moment when he breaks off work on the report to exclaim: "But why, in heaven's name, do *I* have to present this report in Rome—or make this speech in Helsinki! My job is to be a physicist, to work with my hands in a laboratory; I have two theses to correct, this article to read, my lectures at the Collège de France to prepare. . . ."

But no doubt at this moment he remembers the brief exchange which he overheard one day between Irène and their young son Pierre, when he was going off to take part in an election meeting:

"It's not his job to go and make a speech in this school playground," Pierre objected.

"Perhaps it is just because it's not his job that he has more chance of getting people to listen to him," Irène replied.[12]

Then Joliot takes another cigarette. He gazes at his colleague across the flame of his lighter and replies out loud to his own question. "If I want to be able to carry out research tomorrow, if I want young people to be able to devote themselves to it in better conditions and without anxiety—then a society must be created which will recognize the role of science, a society in which war will be not only impossible, but unthinkable. Langevin, too, often told me that he would have preferred to devote all his time to physics. Let us go on."

The next day the first draft, already typed out, is revised. Gradually the edifice is constructed, the conclusion is reached. The day after that, or a few days later, Frédéric Joliot-Curie will be bringing to a conclusion his speech to the World Peace Council. Another brick has been added to the wall being built to contain the threat of war.

It is no exaggeration to say that from 1950 until his death in 1958 the campaign against the danger of nuclear arms was Frédéric Joliot-Curie's major preoccupation.

The declaration he published on January 13, 1955, ends with the following paragraph:

[12] On December 13, 1960, Laurent Casanova, recalling the Buffalo demonstration in April, 1949, said: "Joliot-Curie, Picasso, Aragon! It was a happy chance that enabled those three to be present. The effect on the masses was profound because there was something very unusual in this spectacle of three men leading a popular movement, for whom politics, in the normal sense of the term, was not the first interest in their lives."

The question is not one of which level of military command or which minister or council of ministers—with or without a veto—may decide the issue of atomic war. The question is whether humanity will accept the ruin and the destruction, the death of hundreds of millions of people, the sufferings of the survivors, the probable birth of monsters—and even the possibility of the annihilation of all life on this planet.

He was also anxious to offer a way out to those who did not accept the prospect of waiting in terror for the destructive cataclysm to occur.

Public opinion must be informed as precisely as possible of the extent of the danger and *at the same time* offered solutions which make it possible to ward off the perils. Even in the most dangerous situations there is no panic when everyone knows the road he must take in order to avoid a catastrophe. This road exists—we shall never tire of repeating—it exists necessarily, because although we are faced with immense forces, they are forces liberated by man, and man has complete power to direct their use exclusively for peaceful ends. The situation would be quite different if we had to deal with a brutal threat from natural forces such as that offered by the forecast of an imminent collision between our planet and an immense meteorite.[13]

The danger to humanity was a double one and Joliot never ceased fighting it on both fronts. First, the stockpiling of atomic and hydrogen bombs was in itself a threat to peace and he denounced as fallacious the argument that the horror of a further war would be enough to make such a war impossible.

Yet the monstrous character of modern weapons is often invoked in support of a false and dangerous line of reasoning which runs as follows: a nuclear war would be so horrible that no one will ever dare to start one and peace will thus be maintained by "the balance of terror." The seeming simplicity of this argument has given it a currency which may, if we are not careful, risk leading us straight to disaster.[14]

The second danger was that research carried out in order to perfect these nuclear and thermonuclear weapons made

[13] National Council of the French Peace Movement, Drancy, April 8, 1955.
[14] Frédéric Joliot-Curie's message to the International Congress for Disarmament and International Cooperation in Stockholm, July 16, 1958.

it necessary to hold a series of test explosions. These tests scatter radioactive products in the atmosphere which run the risk of having very harmful effects, not only on people alive today but also on the unborn.

The movement of protest against these tests began with scientists and then spread to the whole world. March 1, 1954 provided a tragic landmark in the history of the struggle of public opinion against the continuation of nuclear weapon tests, when the testing of a hydrogen bomb at Bikini caused several casualties and one death among the crew of a Japanese fishing boat seventy-five miles away from the site of the test.

On April 16, 1957, Joliot broadcast on the French radio the first of two talks he was asked to give on "The Great Discoveries of Radioactivity." The second talk was to be given on April 23, 1957. It was banned by the government which was alarmed at the following paragraphs concerning the dangers of nuclear weapons tests:[15]

If we are to arrive at an agreement to ban atomic weapons —and it is the fate of humanity which is at stake—we must have the weapons tests stopped immediately.

Grave warnings have repeatedly been given by competent scientists ever since the first nuclear weapons tests were held. . . .

Even in time of peace the danger exists. If nuclear weapons tests are not stopped, the amount of radio strontium in men's bodies—and above all in those of children—will certainly increase sufficiently to cause many cases of bone cancer and leukemia. . . .

Believe me! All of us and our children's children are in great danger, if the nuclear weapons tests are not called to an immediate halt.

One year later the U.S.S.R. finally made a first step in this direction. Joliot emphasized the importance of this act at the end of an article on "The World Campaign Against the Atomic Threat" which appeared in *Le Monde Scientifique*.[16]

The unilateral decision taken by the Soviet government to cease nuclear weapons tests has aroused hopes in the world that this gesture will soon be imitated by the governments of the United States and Great Britain. Public opinion

[15] The complete text was published in *La Nef,* May, 1957.
[16] Vol. II, No. 2, p. 38.

follows attentively the talks now being held with a view to reaching an agreement on this question between the three nuclear powers. There is no doubt about what public opinion wants. It is alert and aware of the threat hanging over humanity and it desires an end to the nuclear weapons tests.

The destructive power of the atomic and hydrogen bombs and the immediate and long-term effects of radioactive fall-out from nuclear tests have been described in detail by a great number of scientific authorities. But there still remains a certain skepticism both in the public mind and among responsible authorities. One of the origins of this skepticism may well be the fact that the people who give the warnings might appear to be not merely scientists but all members of one particular political and philosophical family. Further doubts are caused by the fact that there are still points on which the specialists themselves disagree, as regards the scale of certain of the consequences of atomic explosions. And although the specialist would not for a moment dream of denying the terrible potential danger, these differences, un-justifiably, give birth to a tendency to minimize or remain oblivious to the dangers.

For this reason Joliot had already in 1950 formed the idea of gathering around a table scientists from all countries and of all shades of political and philosophical opinion. On the subject of precise scientific problems it should be possible to reach common agreement. The effect on public opinion would be great, for it would then be able to demand that governments everywhere should propose or accept measures designed to preserve the future of mankind.

The task was an extremely difficult one, for the climate of the cold war and of the "witch hunt" made many Western scientists hesitate to meet colleagues from the Soviet Union, or even those of their own compatriots who were classified as "Reds." But Joliot did not give up the attempt.

A decisive turning point in these difficult negotiations was reached when, having learned of a talk broadcast by the British philosopher Bertrand Russell in December, 1954, Joliot wrote to him on January 31, 1955. In his reply Bertrand Russell at once indicated that he was in favor of a joint declaration by scientists on condition that "the signatories should have no common political complexion and that their declaration should strenuously abstain from any blame to either side for past mistakes or what were thought as such." At first, however, he expressed doubts as to the necessity or the possibility of calling an international scientific conference within a useful period of time. On April 5, 1955, having finally accepted the idea of such a conference, Bertrand Russell approached several colleagues, including Einstein, and submitted a draft declaration to them.

On April 20, 1955, Bertrand Russell came to Paris and had a long conversation with Joliot, at the end of which the respective positions of the two men were considerably closer. Bertrand Russell had begun by making his general position clear. Joliot later summarized Russell's words to his friends as follows: "I am an anti-Communist and it is precisely because you are a Communist that I am anxious to work with you."

The correspondence between the two men continued. The most important letters were the one written by Joliot on May 13, 1955, to Bertrand Russell and the latter's reply of June 17. (The text of these letters is given on pages 177-185.[17]) Finally the text of the appeal was approved by Einstein during the last week of this great man's life and was published by Bertrand Russell on Saturday, July 9, 1955, at a press conference at Paxton Hall, London.

Joliot had given his agreement to this text, which is universally known as the Einstein-Russell declaration,* with two important reservations: the first one specified that "limitations of national sovereignty should be agreed to by all, and be in the interests of all." The second reservation concerned the proposition that governments should renounce war; Joliot wanted the words "as a means of settling differences between states" to be added, so as not to condemn movements seeking to fight injustices within a nation, or wars of independence fought by subject peoples.

In fighting with such passion for a ban on atomic weapons and for ending of nuclear weapons tests, Joliot was not simply motivated by his concern for the preservation of the human race. He had devoted his life to science and contributed to the progress of science: from this he had derived the deepest and purest joy. He described this joy to a Portuguese journalist who interviewed him on the subject of his discovery of artificial radioactivity: "I felt a child's

---

[17] These letters are published with the agreement of Lord Russell, to whom I should like to express my sincere thanks.

* This led eventually to holding of the "Pugwash" conferences of scientists of different nations in 1957 and subsequently.—Tr.

joy: I began to run and jump about in that vast basement which was empty at the time. I thought of the consequences which might follow from this discovery."[18]

But joy like this would become impossible if society permitted science to be used for destruction. It had been so difficult throughout the course of history for the scientific spirit to prevail over dogmatic obscurantism that every effort must be now made to prevent the condemnation which should be directed at perversions of science from being leveled at science itself.

It was this double concern to preserve humanity and to defend the good name of science which made him protest against the use of biological weapons. On March 8, 1952, Joliot launched an appeal which called for a halt to the first attempts at bacteriological warfare in the Korean war and the observation of the Geneva Convention of June 17, 1925.

On May 3, 1952, he replied, in passionate terms, to a letter from the United States representative at the U.N., Warren E. Austin:

Before concluding I must tell you that I was struck by the gratuitously insulting tone of your letter. You accuse me of prostituting science because I protest against the criminal use of the discoveries of the great Pasteur and because I appeal to public opinion to prevent the waging of bacteriological warfare.

For me the ones who prostitute science are the people who chose to inaugurate the atomic age by annihilating two hundred thousand civilians at Hiroshima and Nagasaki. . . .

It is because I know all that science can bring to the world that I shall continue my efforts to insure that it contribute to the happiness of all men, whether they be white, black, or yellow, and not to their annihilation in the name of some divine mission or other.

Finally on October 15, 1952, communicating and commenting on the conclusions of the International Scientific Commission of inquiry, he wrote as follows to the presidents of the associations affiliated to the World Federation of Scientific Workers:

It is the duty of scientific workers to inform their fellow citizens in the most appropriate manner of the dangers which threaten humanity from biological weapons and to make known the international agreements on the subject which exist. . . .

It is our duty as scientists to oppose these real perversions of science which run the risk of confusing very many people about science's true function.

[18] The newspaper *Republica,* January 10, 1955.

For science to contribute fully to the happiness of all mankind, the social system must permit its growth and its use for the benefit of all. It was for this reason that Joliot believed in the communist system. But even under the present systems of the civilized world, the absolutely fantastic squandering of wealth due to the production of armaments must be stopped. With perhaps as much energy as he devoted to the struggle to ban atomic weapons, Joliot also campaigned for general disarmament. In this respect his last speech to the Peace Movement—a speech he was unable to deliver himself—may be considered as a testament, in which he dwelt at length on his two main preoccupations.

As he had done at the Pleyel Congress and the Rome Assembly, he first examined the failures of the attempts to reach disarmament which had been made before the First World War.

We cannot forget that the history of disarmament in the first half of the twentieth century is one of many efforts, many hopes, many promises, but also of many disappointments. If we take only the years following the First World War, we must remember the "Kellogg-Briand" pact, signed on August 27, 1928, by nine powers, including the United States, France, Great Britain, Germany, and Italy. Other countries, including the Soviet Union, were later invited to sign and associated themselves with it. The signatories condemned the recourse to war as a means of settling differences between nations and undertook to employ only peaceful means for these ends.

There is no doubt that these agreements, accompanied by declarations and solemn ceremonies, corresponded to the desire of the peoples. But the very best declarations are only of value if they are backed with concrete actions. In this case the convincing concrete action would have been the signature of a disarmament agreement.

In 1929 world expenditure for direct military purposes absorbed $4,200,000,000. In 1957 it had reached $100,000,-000,000—$60,000,000,000 for the NATO countries, $30,-000,000,000 for the socialist countries, and more than $6,000,000,000 for the underdeveloped countries.

Of course the "profits" derived from this production are an inducement to maintain it, and Joliot emphasizes this:

We are aware that for some people the development of weapons is "good business." Armaments, particularly today, when they go out of date so quickly, guarantee certain orders, without hazards, without the risks of competition. And furthermore, the necessary investments, often considerable, are financed by taxes and thus those who are, in the great majority, opposed to the arms race must see a portion of their income taken from them to support it.

Joliot next analyzed the fear that unemployment and an economic crisis would follow if a considerable proportion of the hundred million men directly or indirectly involved in arms production lost their jobs.

We know that only a part of the astronomic sums spent on arms would suffice to finance the employment of all these workers, technicians, and engineers on the production of consumer goods. . . .

Schools, housing, bridges, roads, dams—will they not provide enough to put into effect the necessary adaptation of the factories which squander so much human effort for the sake of war?

It is necessary therefore, not simply to make known the threat of war, which is implicit in the arms race, not only to make fully known all the wealth which the abandoning of this race will make it possible to liberate, but also to dispel the fears which have hitherto prevented popular pressure being sufficient to overcome the resistance of vested intrests:

. . . The sincere acceptance of peaceful coexistence will lead to disarmament, but this is only possible if one abolishes the reasons which are invoked to try to justify the arms race. To this end one must not simply approach the question of disarmament in isolation. It must be intimately linked with the questions of international cooperation and a détente. It seems to me particularly necessary to examine the question of disarmament in relation to economic questions. One must give exact and detailed proof of the fact that the end of the cold war and the arms race would lead to an increase in the standard of living of all nations, *whatever their economic and social system, and I stress this point.*

Just as Joliot always opposed those who invoked a future life to justify and support social injustices in this one, so he many times insisted on the fact that the scientific discoveries already made make it possible *here and now* to lighten the burdens on men's lives and suppress poverty—and it is only the desire to maintain existing privileges which reserves the benefits of science for the minority.

It is not a question of a utopian but unrealistic picture, or of a dream for a distant future. If we but choose to do so, we can make it into the reality of tomorrow.

7

The End of a Life Directed Toward the Future

ON JULY 14, 1951, Irène and Frédéric Joliot-Curie were celebrating the French national holiday with an intimate dinner in the company of Madame Eugénie Cotton. The table was decorated in red, white, and blue, and Irène in a light-hearted mood improvised songs on themes taken from Breton folklore. This scene did not take place at Arcouest but twenty-five miles from Moscow: not far away from this French group A. Vishinsky was playing chess interminably.

Their stay at this rest house had been very pleasant and Joliot often recounted later that his only serious problem had been getting meat grilled "à la française" in place of the excellent meat they were given—which was far too well cooked for his taste.

A few days before, on July 4th, in a hall in the Kremlin, the academician Dmitri Skobeltsin had awarded Joliot the first of the international peace prizes. In his reply Joliot remarked:

For all men of goodwill in the world, whether in the capitalist or the socialist countries, the creation of international prizes for peace provides a concrete proof of the eager desire for peace which is shared by the government and the people of the Soviet Union.

Madame Eugénie Cotton was also among the first nine prizewinners and her delight at receiving this high distinction at the same time as Joliot was only equaled by his own at finding himself in the company of this great lady for whom he felt as much respect as affection.

Less than two years later Joliot was to suffer the first assault of illness. In May, 1953, he had gone to Strasbourg in the company of René Lucas in order to take part in the meetings of the administrative council of the Institute of Nuclear Physics. He went to the hospital for a time, but then resumed his work. In 1955 the illness returned and he had to undergo a long course of treatment at the Saint-Antoine hospital in Paris. He divided his forced leisure between mathematics (as he had done at the time of his operation for appendicitis in 1926) and drawing with pencil and chalk. He had long conversations with Doctor Jacques Caroli, who ran the hospital, and a firm friendship, based on mutual esteem, quickly grew up between them. When he left the hospital he sent Doctor Caroli not only a pencil drawing but also a memorandum in which he proposed improvements in certain methods of observation and in the methods used in the treatment which he had undergone successfully.

It was also at that time that he acquired a new interest in painting. At Antony, in the Auvergne, and in Brittany he painted several pictures of the landscapes which were dear to him. Although his health was improving slowly but surely, he was compelled, if not to cut down his activities, at least to travel less. He spent a great deal of time at Antony and was visited by many people. The workers from his laboratory came to see him there. But neither reading nor conversations were enough for him. He missed working with his hands.

In order to satisfy this real need, he had a small laboratory fitted up at his house, as well as a dark room for photography, and, most important, a small mechanical workshop with a lathe and a drill. In this way he was able to carry out at home experiments relating to the evidence he was asked to give as an expert witness in a notorious poisoning case, and also some research into the comparative strontium content of condensed milk of recent and older dates with a view to studying the effects of radioactive fallout from nuclear weapons tests.

His strength gradually returned to him. He was able to go skiing that winter at Courcheval, as he had done every year before, and to go fishing in the summer at Arcouest. Nevertheless the idea of his death preoccupied him very much, and he often told me of his conviction that he had not long to live. Despite appearances, he felt his illness had left its mark on him and he was sure he would die long before Irène. He told me these things very objectively and it is only at this distance that I perceive his need to confide in someone and his hope of receiving a reassuring denial.

On March 17, 1956, Irène Joliot-Curie died of leukemia, which was without a doubt the result of long years of work in the presence of radiation from radioactive substances and of the months spent in the radiological service with the armies in the First World War.

Joliot had recognized the origins of Irène's illness, but he would not admit that his own liver complaint resulted from his exposure to radiation. When this point was discussed he emphasized the great care he had always taken to protect himself and the insistence with which he had always made his co-workers do the same. Only careless haste on the part of laboratory workers, or in industrial economies made at the expense of safety made this work dangerous, and he was angered by the notion of erroneous conclusions being drawn from his illness in order to discourage research workers from following his own chosen path.

The death of his wife came as a severe blow to him and caused him to ask himself once again about the sense of the work he had accomplished with Irène. It was then that he wrote his essay on "The Human Value of Science," a text in which the whole of his personality can best be seen.[1]

The awareness of the influence—whether great or small—which the time spent by each one of us on this earth will certainly have on future generations led me in adolescence to adopt a more serene attitude in the face of death. Every man has a reflex of refusal at the thought of death being followed by nothingness. The idea of nothingness is so intolerable that men have sought refuge in the belief in another world dominated by one or several gods.

By nature a rationalist, I refused at an early age to accept this baseless and tenuous belief.

What terrible disillusionments I have witnessed in those who have suddenly lost their faith! But, why—I was about to say: why the devil—imagine survival in another world? My own preoccupation in the face of death very early came down to a purely human and terrestrial problem. Does not eternity lie in the living and perceptible chain which links us with the things which have been done and the beings that have lived on this earth?

I will refer, if you will forgive me, to a personal memory. As a schoolboy I was one evening doing my homework. As I worked, my hand played with the stem of a brass candle-

[1] This essay appeared in *La Nef*, No. 2, January, 1957, and is printed in full on pages 144-152.

stick, a very old family heirloom. I broke off writing with a start, having felt a strong emotion. With closed eyes I was conjuring up scenes which this old candlestick had no doubt witnessed—a trip down to the cellar to find a bottle of wine to celebrate a happy anniversary, the sad watch over a dead person. . . . I had the impression of coming into contact with the hands which had carried this candlestick over the centuries; I made out faces. I found great solace in this evocation of dead people with whom I experienced a feeling of close solidarity. Pure imagination, of course, but the object caused me to evoke unknown dead people, whom I saw as living, and my fear of nothingness was banished from my mind once and for all.

Every being who passes on earth leaves an indelible mark, even if it is only a little wood worn away by their hand on a railing, a little stone worn away from a step. I love wood polished through use, steps hollowed by human feet; I love my old brass candlestick. . . . They have an eternity in them.

After Irène's death—even in the periods when he seemed to have recovered his good health—Joliot gave all those who worked with him the impression of racing against the clock, against time. He wanted at all costs to see the laboratories at Orsay, south of Paris, completed.

In order to replace the premises of the Radium Institute which had grown too small, Irène Joliot-Curie had suggested to the Faculty of Science at Paris that a new set of buildings be built. Thanks to the very active support of the Dean, A. Chatelet, the construction of a first set of buildings was decided on in July, 1955.

The natural setting in the tranquillity of the green countryside is favorable to fundamental research. Nevertheless the clay soil necessitated very detailed survey work on the land which would in places have to support very heavy loads, such as accelerators and concrete screens for protection against the dangers of radiation. It took about six months for the foundations to be laid and the buildings to begin to emerge above ground level. Irène Joliot-Curie, who had given so much of her energy toward the realization of this work, unfortunately never had the joy of witnessing this birth.[2]

He was at first apprehensive of taking on the additional

_____
[2] "The New Orsay Center." Lecture given by F. Joliot-Curie at the meeting of the Nobel prize winners at Lindau (June 30-July 3, 1958).

burden of succeeding to his wife as Professor of the Faculty of Science of Paris and Director of the Curie Laboratory and the Radium Institute, but he finally decided to submit his candidacy. His appointment in September, 1956, saw him combining the posts of Professor of the Faculty of Science and Professor at the Collège de France, the precedent for which was Claude Bernard. With the same energy he began supervising the new construction work, a task with which he had already had some experience. He presided over meetings of architects, visited the sites, summoned contractors—all this in addition to his talks with research workers, visits to ministries, and political and social work.

In August, 1957, the construction of the first section of buildings was completed, and although the interior fittings were not yet finished, Joliot decided in September to move the laboratory workers to Orsay. In his haste he even cut short his own summer holidays in Brittany and returned to Paris—several days too soon, for his own office was not ready for him!

Less than a year later, when he described this group of laboratories in detail to the thirteen Nobel Prize winners assembled with him at Lindau on the shores of Lake Constance, Joliot was able to say, with some pride: "At the moment about 250 people are working in our group at Orsay and Paris, of whom 90 are qualified research workers and 150 are technicians—which is a large team for a laboratory engaged on fundamental research."

Before going to Lindau, Joliot, whose health was improving, had been able to resume his trips abroad. In April, 1957, he had gone to the meeting of the Bureau of the World Peace Council in Berlin[3] and in May, 1958, he went to Moscow. He had an interview with Premier Khrushchev, and visited many laboratories, notably that at Dubna, where he was delighted to meet Bruno Pontecorvo again. Finding himself with someone who reminded him of his days in the laboratory before the war, he confided the dream which he hoped to see realized: "In a year's time I shall be rid of all my administrative duties and I shall be able to perform experiments with my own hands again."

He also had long talks with colleagues he liked and greatly respected, such as Blokhintsev, Kurchatov, Skobeltsin, and Infeld. He was welcomed by the Soviet Peace Movement

[3] For the first time in several years he made this journey alone.

and was able to spend an evening at the home of his friend Ilya Ehrenburg. On his return, in the Tupolev plane which brought him back to France, he communicated his impressions to his friend Roger Mayer. After telling him how much he had been impressed by what he had seen, by the equipment, and above all by the young generation of scientists, he concluded: "However, I have no reason to be ashamed of Orsay and I would not swap my team for any other."

One recognizes in this remark his confidence in his own country, his pride in France's contribution to civilization, his desire to insure that her future live up to her past. Joliot feared that the younger generation, as well as the public authorities, were not sufficiently aware of France's importance in the field of science. That is why on December 14, 1954, in his reply to a questionnaire drawn up by the higher education authorities, he had written on the subject of scientific missions abroad:

In conclusion, if one wants real knowledge to come from this mission, it is necessary to send abroad men who have already made tangible contributions in their own country and who have a broad knowledge of the material equipment and men existing in France. One will thus avoid the inferiority complexes of those who are more ignorant of their own country than they should be, and who sometimes return from abroad bringing back knowledge which the French have already exported.

In his lecture at Lindau he returned once more to the theme of the importance of scientific traditions.

We strive to preserve the precious traditions of our masters in the subject of radioactivity. It is risky to improvise in this field, although it is one which may appear simple and often seems old-fashioned to nuclear physicists who have no knowledge of it.

Research workers who go to laboratories which have old traditions often profit unbeknown to themselves from what I call their "hidden wealth." Ideas put out at the laboratory in the past by masters and research workers—who may or may not still be alive—recur periodically in conversation and are absorbed consciously or unconsciously by the youngest research workers. In the course of a piece of work these acquired ideas facilitate a correct interpretation and sometimes a discovery. This helps one to understand better why a given discovery had the best chance of being made at a given laboratory.

When the British scientist C. F. Powell was examining Joliot's scientific work on June 29, 1959, in London, he remarked particularly:

"In a sense Joliot and others were pioneers along a new road in the evolution of science, a road which leads to the fusion of academic and industrial experimentation. In a sense it was the start of a great development which transformed experimentation in the scientific field. In the following twenty-five years the scale of experiment became greater and greater and research took on more and more of the characteristics of a big industrial enterprise."

This transformation of the character of physical research was one of the matters which deeply preoccupied Joliot during his last years. Looking back over his thirty years as a laboratory worker and considering the almost "monstrous" installations needed by physicists today, he posed the question, at the end of his Lindau paper, of the problem of adapting one's personality to these new working surroundings.

The text of this report, which is reproduced on page 143, merits study and reflection. It is in some sense the great scientist's last appeal—passionately devoted to his profession as he was—to all his colleagues to study a new and serious problem posed by scientific progress itself.[4]

Those who have miraculously escaped a fatal accident often tell of having seen images of the most significant moments of their lives flash through their minds. The activities of the last weeks of Frédéric Joliot's life covered the broad and rich spectrum of his major preoccupations and favorite activities.

On his return from the U.S.S.R. Joliot had for the last time taken part in a public demonstration, one organized at the Sorbonne in protest against the coup of May 13, 1958.

At the Institut Henri-Poincaré he had a meeting with Colleagues from the university and won a victory—not without some difficulty—for his conception of the teaching program which was being planned at the C.E.A.

After putting the finishing touches to the speech he had written for the International Congress for Disarmament and International Cooperation (Stockholm, July 16-21, 1958) and inaugurating and presiding over the International Con-

---

[4] See on this subject the symposium organized by the Association Frédéric et Irène Joliot-Curie and published in the magazine *Sciences*, December, 1960.

gress of Nuclear Physics in Paris, he set off for Arcouest by car. Previous to this (his last contact with the World Federation of Scientific Workers), he had received—in the study which had belonged first to Marie Curie, then to André Debierne and then to Irène before becoming his own—his Bulgarian friend, Professor Kyril Bratanov in the company of Doctor Boyadjieff. They talked of the early days of the World Federation of Scientific Workers, of a bus that broke down in the middle of the night on a journey in Czechoslovakia in 1948. They made plans for a bear hunt in Bulgaria in the summer of 1959.

On the last Saturday of July, 1958, Roger Mayer, on his return from Stockholm, was held up at Dinant by a breakdown. Joliot came to fetch him in his car and asked him about the Congress. During all these last months the completion and starting up of the Orsay laboratory had hardly preoccupied him more than the desire to see established the necessary connection between economic problems and those of disarmament and peace.

"The children are away on a cruise," he explained to Roger Mayer, "so we can take the boat. We shall be quiet and we can write something more elaborate about these questions."

On Sunday night, after working with his boatman taking in the nets, he went to call on his friends the Ségals. Sitting on the floor among the children, while the other adults sat on chairs, he listened delightedly as Francis Lemarque sang to the guitar (with the apology that the presence of the "kids" might somewhat limit his repertoire).

On Monday he went fishing at four o'clock in the morning. On his return he was visited by the inspector of boats who examined the ship's articles and congratulated him—to his great satisfaction—on having maintained his ship's medicine chest in perfect order.

It was on the Tuesday night that a hemorrhage took him by surprise and made him cry out: "I am done for!"

At nine o'clock the next morning, recovered now but still alarmed, he left his house in Arcouest. Lying on the stretcher, he looked at the bay and the rocks. He saw the boatman whom he had arranged to meet before dawn. He said nothing, but the people with him, who knew and loved him, read in his eyes a last farewell to the trees he had planted, to the terrace he had consolidated and enlarged—to this corner of the world which he preferred to all others. All the way to the train station at Saint-Brieuc, lying in the ambulance and looking out at the road, he commented in a few words on the familiar scenes which went past him and his companions.

On their arrival at the Gare Montparnasse an ambulance was waiting and his companions tried to arrange for it to be brought onto the platform, alongside the carriage. The authorities objected. Negotiations were about to break down when the engine driver declared, without anyone having approached him, that he, for his part, would refuse to shift his train until the ambulance for Professor Joliot-Curie was allowed to come and remove him.

At the Saint-Antoine hospital his strength returned and he spent several days writing out the last pages of his course of lectures on radioactivity—which were destined to be published for the students. He corrected the proofs of an article for *L'Age Nucléaire*. His morale and his physical condition improved greatly and he was looking forward to returning to Britanny on August 12, 1958.

On August 14, 1958, the man whose "work in the field of nuclear physics won him a place among the greatest scientists of the world and whose work as a man ensured him a place in history,"[5] died.

[5] C. F. Powell, speech in London, June 22, 1959.

8

Joliot: Rationalist and Communist

ON JUNE 6, 1950, when he saw Roger Mayer who was to be his secretary and who rapidly became his friend, Joliot was anxious to make one thing immediately clear: "I am not an intellectual: I am too fond of working with my hands to be that. Furthermore there is one word I never like to hear used in my presence and that is 'philosophy'."

As Jean Orcel has rightly observed, "Joliot's irony was directed more at the adepts of metaphysical thought than at general philosophical reflection on the systems of modern science and the conclusions that are bound to follow from it." Indeed in 1931 Joliot and I had ourselves published an essay on "The Philosophy of Henri Poincaré,"[1] which begins as follows:

Henri Poincaré, who was passionately devoted to science, considered that it should be the sole basis of all thought and had no faith in any theory which did not rely, more or less closely, on the study of nature. He had held this attitude from a very early age and, in the course of an interview he was kind enough to grant us, Monsieur Raymond Poincaré told us that when he was a student of arts his cousin continually made gibes about the value of his metaphysical studies. Science, for Henri Poincaré, should alone rule our actions, and, not content with his contributions to science as a mathematician and physicist of genius, he also sought to study it as a philosopher.

Frédéric Joliot was profoundly rationalist. He showed this in many articles and lectures—and in succeeding Paul Langevin as President of the Rationalists' Union. One day in May, 1953, when he was presiding over a lecture given by Paul Laberenne and Evry Schatzmann on the four hundred-and-tenth anniversary of the death of Copernicus, he said:[2]

[1] F. Joliot and P. Biquard, *Anthologie des philosophes français contemporains,* published by Kra, pp. 50-76.

[2] Text published in the *Lettres Françaises,* June 4, 1953.

The work of Nicholas Copernicus, a scientist whose genius was universal, a great humanist and a patriot, constitutes a revolutionary act which had far-reaching effects. To make the sun the center of the planetary system was to fly in the face of all the science inherited from antiquity as well as the teachings of the Scriptures. It was heresy to state that the earth was not the center of the universe. The Church would not admit this. It was a fruitful act of liberation of the human spirit, which for more than twenty centuries had been stifled and clouded by superstition and dogmas. But these superstitions and dogmas were spread and inexorably maintained by the few people for whom they were a source of profit and a basis for power. In that great movement of liberation which was the Renaissance, Copernicus struck a hard blow at the obscurantist authorities and shook the foundations of a power which for thousands of years had held society in chains.

This rationalist attitude was to attract him progressively to the study of social problems and the continuation and expansion of the rationalism of Descartes and the materialism of the eighteenth-century Encyclopedists.

Our modern rationalism is not a mere enrichment of that of the past. It is resolutely derived from Marxism, from the doctrine discovered by Marx and Engels at a time when, owing to the place occupied by the working class in society, it posed so many problems that it called for a specific ideology.

"They could have forgiven me any error," Frédéric Joliot often said to me, "any crime—but not that of being a Communist. I was born into a middle-class family. I received a good education. I have been successful. I am comfortably off. In their eyes I have no excuse and the ostracism I am subjected to has no other origin than this."

Joliot was profoundly Communist. His family background, despite its relative prosperity, had predisposed him to be very liberal and generous in his attitudes. For this reason it is hardly surprising that he joined the League of the Rights of Man and the Citizen, the Socialist Party, the Anti-Fascist Intellectuals' Vigilance Committee, and other organizations. Paul Langevin's influence confirmed him in this path, but it is interesting to note that he joined the Communist Party before his teacher. When he was invited to give his reasons for joining in 1946, he replied:

The examination of past history and of the living conditions of societies today, from the points of view of science and of human solidarity, have led me naturally to communism. The Communist Party is the only one which fights in a "coherent" manner against fascism and against egoistical and conservative minorities, for more liberty, progress, and justice. The Communist Party greatly stimulates individual initiative in order that the fruits of labor shall be used to the full for the material and moral well-being of mankind. In this it satisfies our double duty to the individual personality and to human solidarity.

There are few of his friends or even of his acquaintances who did not hear from his own mouth his motives for this choice, the consequences of which he understood perfectly well. He explained to his biographer, Michel Rouzé in 1950:[3]

What is it that differentiates man from the animals? It is the fact that when he wakes up he does not simply think about hunting for food—or rather a day will come when he will not be able to think simply of that. At present millions of men on the earth are forced to live like animals, to concentrate on hunting for food for themselves and their families. Even myself. . . .

This is not civilization. It is not true that the work imposed on us by our need to eat is moral work. "In the sweat of thy face shalt thou eat bread"—I want none of this philosophy. It is taught by exploiters—those who live off the work of other people. Should not science and technology enable us to have to do very little work in order to eat? We shall be civilized when man no longer needs to work as he does now in order to insure his survival. This does not mean he will do nothing. On the contrary, it is only then that his work will become moral, when he does additional, voluntary work with his brain or his hands, in order to make a contribution to others, to enrich the life of humanity.

In the same way he often emphasized, in the course of many conversations, the importance of "democratic centralism," which makes for the rule of true democracy within the Communist Party. This was not simply a sentimental reflex of generosity—it was first and foremost the application of the scientific method to the problems of society which concerned him.

Thus on January 28, 1948, addressing the *Amis de la Pensée (Friends of Thought),* he analyzed the role of Karl Marx's *Das Kapital:*

[3] *F. Joliot-Curie* by Michel Rouzé, p. 52.

The continued validity of the opinions and conclusions and the richness of the teaching which we find in this work, as in those of all the great philosophers, are due, no doubt, to the rigor and the precision of the whole scientific method which he defined and applied to the study of social phenomena.

Let us note, too, this passage from the message he addressed to the fourteenth Congress of the French Communist Party (quoted on p. 174):

Today the immense progress due to Marx can be seen in all its power and scope. By using the scientific method, Marx was able to distinguish the most important laws of the evolution of human societies.

In comparing the possibilities of action which are offered to men by the various social systems, it is important to distinguish between the factors which are due to human nature, to men's very diverse intellectual and moral qualitites, and those which are inherent in the social system in which a man lives and acts:

Under the capitalist system, a man with all possible personal qualities but acting in the service of capitalism and applying its rules is perpetually placed in situations where, at best, he can choose the solution which is the least harmful to the great majority of his fellow citizens and to his country. For basically his conduct is determined not by his personal qualities, but by the system itself.

The socialist system never puts those who serve it in such situations. Whether good or harm results from their actions depends on their own qualities and not on the system. And as it is a question of human qualities, society is able either to change the man or to replace him.

In the same way an excellent scientist, reasoning logically, but from incorrect premises, cannot arrive at correct conclusions. If the premises are correct, whether he reaches true or false conclusions will depend entirely on the scientist's own abilities, and we shall be able to judge him accordingly and decide whether to put our trust in him or not.

He was also often angered by the fraudulent use made of the word "liberty" by the critics of communism:

We, more than anyone else, are devoted to liberty, not the liberty which consists of exploiting one's fellowmen, not the liberty which can reach accommodation with the capitalist system, but liberty free of all hypocrisy, uncontaminated by any lies.

We have too much respect for this word, "liberty," to use it lightly. Liberty will be won by our efforts in common.

We desire to see the disappearance of the social injustices, the poverty, the lies, the degradation and the moral impoverishment which are inherent in the capitalist system. By joining forces with those who suffer most directly from these injustices we put ourselves in a position to contribute to their disappearance. Our liberty comes from the inspiring feeling that we can be effective.

Apart from his historical analysis and his study of the laws which operate in societies, he found confirmation for his convictions in looking at the evolution of the U.S.S.R. since 1917.

At the time when the Tsarist regime and then the bourgeois democratic regime, overthrown by the joint action of the workers and the peasants, were collapsing and leaving the way open for the power of the Soviets, Joliot was twenty-seven. Like all young men he was open to new ideas and was filled with enthusiasm for the social experiment which was being carried out amid tragic conditions. Like all the young people of that period he was subjected to a heavy barrage of propaganda angled against a working and peasant class which had dared to liberate itself. He often said he would like to see a collection of all the dire predictions which were made about the future of the Bolshevik regime, all the proofs offered by "the most distinguished economists" to the effect that it could not possibly survive, etc. . . .

On the day on which the launching of the first artificial earth satellite opened the eyes of those who had hitherto believed all these authoritative or inspired statements, Joliot gave the following explanations, which appeared in *Pravda* on October 17, 1957:

But the satellite has faced the scientists of the United States, England, and France with a much more serious question: why precisely has the Soviet Union, with its scientists and technicians, succeeded in getting there first? . . .

It must be said that some people were ready for such a question and others were not. Those who had had contacts with the Soviet scientists knew of the extraordinarily rapid development of science and technology in the Soviet Union. But that is not all. Account should have been taken of the fact that in the U.S.S.R. the whole people are engaged in a gigantic task and that they understand that the liberation of man and a real increase in the welfare of men demand gigantic efforts in the fields of science and technology. And furthermore one must take into account what one may call the "development curve for Soviet science and technology" over the course of the last decades. This "curve" could not have passed unnoticed by any impartial observer who had revisited the Soviet Union after an interval of several years. . . .

The fact that it was the Soviet Union which was the first to launch a satellite is not at all a matter of chance. This lead over Western science will be accentuated from year to year. Even the paths taken in the development of science and technology in the socialist countries differ from those taken in the others.

It seemed to him undeniable that errors, even very grave ones, and crimes had been committed, but he was convinced that in the socialist system possibilities for correcting these existed, by the very nature of the system itself, and the work of the twentieth congress of the Communist Party of the Soviet Union brought him decisive confirmation of this.

Finally his belief was strengthened as his visits to the U.S.S.R. showed him the rapidly rising curve of progress. He went to the Soviet Union in 1933, in 1936, in 1945, in 1949, in 1951, and finally in 1958, three months before his death. Was it fate that wanted to give him, on this last visit, a brilliant confirmation of the confidence he had always expressed in the Soviet Union's capacity for progress? At all events he spent two and a half hours at the Kremlin on this occasion with Premier Khrushchev. Only one of the latter's close colleagues and an interpreter were with them.

The interview was interrupted at one moment by the ringing of the telephone. Khrushchev ignored it and went on talking. Somebody knocked on the door, came in, and said a few words. Then Khrushchev lifted the receiver and after several seconds his face broke into a broad smile. Putting the receiver down he got up and exclaimed something. He struck Joliot vigorously on the shoulder with his hand and with the other hand he made large circles in the air. The interpreter then explained: the third Sputnik had just been put into orbit!

9

The Man

WHEN THE name of Archimedes is mentioned, who does not immediately picture a distracted scientist leaping from his bath dressed in the simplest attire, with a cry of "Eureka!"?

Copernicus and Galileo make us think of the first correct interpretation given to the astronomers' observations and, also, of the vain struggle of the Church against the discoveries of science.

The name of Newton inevitably suggests a falling apple, while that of Pasteur is always associated with the picture in all the school books of the great scientist with the young boy he saved from hydrophobia. These immediate images will then give way to reflections about the path Newton took in order to arrive at his laws of gravitation or to the sequence of investigations which led Pasteur to study the attenuation of viruses after he had started out doing research on crystallography.

One wonders what the thoughts on the mind of a physicist of tomorrow or even further ahead will be when he comes upon this reference in the course of a piece of bibliographical research:

Joliot F. and Curie I.

1) Artificial production of radioactive elements.

2) Chemical proof of the transmutation of elements, *J. Phys.*, 5, 153, 1934.

Having obtained the bound volume of the *Journal de Physique* he may perhaps break off his reading and allow his mind to wander for a moment. He will picture the young couple photographed in white coats in front of an apparatus which many people wrongly regard as being already out of date. And if he has already studied Frédéric Joliot's scientific work in detail, the thought may once again cross his mind that as his pupil Bruno Pontecorvo has so well expressed it: "This physicist possessed in the highest degree what the Italians call *spregindicatezza*—the ability to recognize as possible even the most strange and impossible facts."

If our scientist is himself concerned by the social implications of science and technology he will be glad to learn that at a particularly critical time there should have been a man like Frédéric Joliot to give a full definition to the duty of the true servants of science. If he does not share Joliot's philosophical and political opinions perhaps his thoughts may be something like those of one his pupils and colleagues, Francis Suzor:[1]

For those who did not share his opinions, there is a risk that his reputation as a scientist will be tarnished by the actions of the political man. But in every field he showed the same rigor and honesty of judgment without which, despite his intuitive genius, none of his discoveries in nuclear physics would have been possible. His generous spirit made him want to give and commit himself totally, and he dedicated himself to the cause which seemed to him to be the best one, that of communism. Myself a Catholic, I had long conversations with him in which we omitted no part of our respective beliefs. His reasons were alien to me, but I appreciated his good faith and kept my affection for him. He told me one day that he had witnessed the sufferings of several of his friends who had lost their faith in Christianity, and added that, for his own part, his conduct and his work left him at peace with himself. All his convictions, which were supported by his reason, were also based on a gigantic extrapolation: he believed that humanity, at hardly a few score generations' remove from prehistory, was still groping, and he was convinced that he was moving in the right direction and for the good of humanity. Having rejected religious faith, he had found another faith to guide his action in which the lofty qualities of his heart and spirit found concrete expression.

For Francis Suzor, as for all the research workers who had the privilege of working under him, Frédéric Joliot was above and before all the "chief," to whom had fallen the difficult task of being responsible for the life of the laboratory and the work of the scientists there.

One aspect of the role of the director of a laboratory often remains unknown to or undervalued by those who benefit

[1] *La Pensée,* September-October, 1959, p. 90.

from it . . . until the day when they accede to the post of director themselves. It is that imposed by dealings with the various administrations. The shortage of funds and the markedly low salaries oblige the director, whose concern is above all for the team to be able to work, to make endless appeals for money and to go through endless contortions of accounting which take up his time and are a strain on his nerves. And when the material conditions are established he has the additional tasks of suggesting projects of work and of following and directing the research. Wrote Pierre Radvanyi:[2]

Joliot was keen to know every sector of life in the laboratory. Once a year he called us all together in order to tell us about general problems, to discuss things that were not going well, to organize this or that sector of the work of laboratory, to discuss tasks which were of general concern and also to introduce new ones. . . .

He insisted that discussion should develop in the course of his talk. "You must not hesitate to interrupt," he would say, "in order to ask for an explanation which will allow you to follow the thread—or in order to ask a question, even one that may seem stupid, or to make a comment." And his method of directing these meetings was extremely stimulating.

But that is still not enough. The director, in addition to meeting groups, discussing results, and establishing programs, must also have personal contact with a great variety of men and women.

Once inside his study one forgot the people who might be waiting their turn outside the door. I must say that, for my part, I never entered his study without my heart beating faster and I never left it without having been given food for thought for several days.

All those who had discussions with Joliot, either alone or in a group, on scientific, political, or artistic subjects, will always have one firm memory. It is that of the moment when he managed to put the problem under discussion into a broader perspective or to throw light on it from a new angle and thus to open up unforeseen possibilities for a solution.

This feeling of having enriched one's own knowledge and vision of the world in his company was at the basis of

[2] *Ibid.*, p. 85.

the profound confidence which his presence was able to inspire.

What could the name of Frédéric Joliot-Curie mean to a workman, a peasant, or a tradesman in France or abroad? There is no doubt about the reply to this question for those who saw the slow pilgrimage of thousands of men and women who for two days came to pay their respects before the catafalque of Frédéric Joliot-Curie in the half-empty Paris of mid-August, 1958. Some people's eyes were filled with tears, others reflected a more stoical self-restraint. Women knelt or crossed themselves, the men bared their heads proudly. They had all come there, their hearts heavy with sadness and filled with gratitude for a scientist whose discoveries meant no more than a word to many people. They paid homage to a scientist who had not simply contributed to the progress of science and worked for the development and prosperity of his country, but who had also been able to leave his ivory tower in order to come and fight in their midst for justice and peace.

For his friends and all those who had lived with him either for long or short periods, "Fred," as everyone called him, was a person with many facets, like all gifted people. He won people over rapidly, for he understood, sympathized with, and loved his fellowmen, provided only that they were sincere.

He was very fond of music and could sit at the piano improvising for hours. He recorded himself on tape and would take mischievous pleasure, when playing it back, in asking his baffled or embarrassed listener if the piece were by Mendelssohn or Beethoven. He liked discussing music, not only with his son, Pierre, but with a musical scholar, his friend George Léon, who has been kind enough to give us his impressions of Joliot, the musician:

Joliot was an artist in the manner of an *honnête homme*. He had the prejudice of discussing and judging only what he knew. He was open to whatever one suggested: a sonata, a song, a pastel drawing, an etching, a symphony.

He had no hatred in him: he had ideas. He felt first and understood afterward. Rather like François Couperin who said: "I prefer what moves me to what surprises me."

Joliot did not have an expert knowledge of music, he simply loved it, and it was really this—his unrestricted openness to whatever was presented—which made this man of science the perfect audience.

He made critical judgments but never before he had heard a thing out. He was enthusiastic, sometimes naïve. He had no "idols," but he had crazes. His only dislikes (I am thinking now about modern music and his comments on it) sprang no doubt from the fact that he had not had the time to devote himself fully to real exploration of the field. These dislikes—though the word is perhaps a little strong—often led to a kind of game. If he contradicted a view it was often in order to learn from someone else. His preference was for Bach, Beethoven, and Mozart. He often spoke of them, listened to them, and sought to convince his friends of his reasons for liking them. And thus he became a combination of the scientist giving a proof, the inspired lover, and the advocate pleading a cause.

Joliot the artist was youth itself. Not in his taste but in his enthusiasm—which could lead him to proselytizing. I will never forget, having once heard him, how he talked, for example, of Bach, whom he had introduced to the fishermen of Arcouest one summer evening.

Nor can one forget how unaffectedly he listened to and thanked the artists who, brought by friends, sometimes came to visit him and ended by performing spontaneously for him. His joy gave pleasure. His sincerity was touching. It was like the welcome he gave. He was a versatile host. He knew how to receive.

If he had had the time to do so, Joliot would have acquired a vast musical culture. He had no patience with half-measures. He could not abide people's making judgments in his presence unsupported by real knowledge. What he required of his friends and the people he talked with he also required of himself. It was advisable for those who came near him to discover this quickly. He applied severe standards to art, to artists, and to his own amusements. That is why he spoke only of what he knew, though he never stopped seeking from other people new reasons for understanding and appreciating something, because he respected hard work and because the conviction with which other people defended tastes which were not his interested him rather than puzzled him.

I had often experienced this, for example, when speaking to him about my taste for modern music. He was not satisfied when one said that one liked a work, a composer. He wanted one's judgment to be fully supported with arguments. If he did not agree his disagreement was rarely absolute. He seldom said "I do not like"—rather, "I do not understand."

His profound intellectual and moral honesty thus led him to listen, to see, and to judge. But he also enjoyed taking part himself—both in music and in painting.

When he sat down at the piano or painted, Joliot was discretion itself. Yet he had prodigious flights of fancy.

We knew that, along with Bach, Mozart, and Beethoven, Mahler was one of his favorite composers. This preference explains the man a good deal more than it might appear to. Those who heard Frédéric Joliot's improvisations at the piano preserve the memory of a natural virtuosity, a phenomenal dexterity. His right hand would sweep up and down in arpeggios, his left maintaining the balance. When he indulged in this "pastime" one felt he approached the tints of Schubert, Mendelssohn, and Chopin. Nothing was calculated, yet everything sounded right.

His love of nature revealed itself in many details. And he became truly the artist as soon as he spoke of mountains or the sea, his boat and the rocks, snow or flowers. There was one flower in particular, which he had preserved for a long time and of which he was proud: he had picked it, he told us, in New York one day, growing between the paving stones.

When he spoke of his amazement one had a revelation of Joliot the poet—and he was always a poet, not from pretentiousness, but simply because that was his nature.

Another of his intimate friends, Jacques Adnet,[3] often spoke to him about poetry:

Fred liked simple works, close to human life, even the most harrowing aspects of it. I remember his mania for Edith Piaf. He was very fond of the poets, but only simple poets, whose work was musical. . . . Poetry was the common denominator for three of us, Irène, Fred, and myself. I can still see Irène reciting Kipling's "If"[4] in a gentle, even voice. He loved authentic lives and authentic people: he accepted their language and quickly got on well with them."

When his illness and convalescence forced Joliot to travel less often, to spend less time at his laboratory, and to take longer holidays he took up painting—naturally with great seriousness. In doing so he was only satisfying an inclination he had acquired during his youth from contact with his sister, the painter of flowers, and the artistic world she moved in. Charles Lapicque has told us:

We often had long conversations about painting. Fred was never able to give much time to educating himself in this field, to visiting exhibitions or museums, so that his taste was

---

[3] Director of the École des Arts décoratifs.
[4] Irène Joliot-Curie translated some of Kipling's poems into French.

generally for works portraying the world in a fairly literal way. He had the honesty and modesty to apologize for this from time to time—particularly when he was painting himself. He sought conscientiously to represent what he saw. This was, he said, the first and necessary stage before embarking on the transposition of appearances. But in fact the paintings he produced do not at all give the impression of experiments, but of finished works which bear witness to an acute feeling for nature: they are not without affinities to those of the painters called "primitives," although in truth the quality of "primitiveness" does not play an important role in either case. This style of painting may rather be traced to a certain quality of being rooted in life. If Beauchant was a gardener, Fred Joliot hunted, sailed, and fished with a passion which left no time for the overlong contemplation of forms, but which in his painting served to infuse the land and the water with a reality which simple contemplation could not have provided. In particular I like his "Landscape in Auvergne" for the feeling of the countryside which it gives, and a view of the bay of Launay, painted from the terrace of his house at Arcouest where the sea, the sky, the boats at anchor, and the Trinité headland are painted with startling actuality.

Although he generally showed little inclination toward strongly nonrepresentational painting, whether ancient or modern, he sometimes understood its mechanisms in a way which was surprising even to the painter. Thus one day, when I was showing him a series of sea paintings on which there were boats surrounded by curves shaped like figure eights representing waves, he sensed at once that these lines were not arbitrary and began to consider their origin. "These lines," he said, after a moment's thought, "are an accurate representation of the movement of the stem post, which is raised vertically as each wave passes, but at the same time carried sideways by the impact of the same wave on the side of the boat. This produces the weaving progress, which is nothing else but a "figure of Lissajous."

I had in fact worked from instinct but his interpretation seemed to me so convincing that I at once made it my own.

There is another type of written evidence which throws a vivid light on the personality of Joliot. As a physicist "he noted down all the details and circumstances of an experiment, including those which at first sight might seem insignificant—and he recommended others to do the same."[5]

Apart from his laboratory notebooks and the page of

[5] Pierre Radvanyi, *La Pensée,* No. 87, p. 87.

the diary already referred to, Joliot's papers contain a little notebook, with squared paper and a blue cover, crammed with small writing which is often difficult to read. Except for three pages of calculations of the "height and time of tides," it is a complete log of all his stays at Arcouest from 1953 to 1956. Day by day he notes the atmospheric conditions, the pressure, the direction of the wind, the state of the sea, the movements of his boats, the wins and losses at the regattas and, above all—the thing that enthused him as much as physics—the results of his fishing expeditions.

Thus on August 24, 1953 he writes:

Pots lifted morning, 10 . . . 1 small lobster. Wind S.W. Very strong, sun, cloud, pressure 759 morning, evening 762.
Thursday 4 August, 1955:
Splendid morning: mild E. wind. Splendid day. Shopping after lunch with Irène at Fournier's. Very fine view over Trieux. Finished communiqué for World Congress. . . . I go to see Labour and he is pleased that I am working with Jean Colin, of whom he speaks very highly.

Labour and Colin were two sailors who had sailed the seven seas. And when Joliot went on board the boat, worked and talked with one of them, each of the two felt he was "with one of the family," in the company of a comrade who knew and loved the sea, who was sensitive to its slightest nuances, who observed the horizon and could interpret a rising breeze or forming clouds. On board the boat they were not Labour the sailor and Joliot the physicist—they were two seamen. In the same way when Joliot was in a factory in France or abroad and stopped to talk to a group of workmen, foremen, or engineers, in a few minutes everyone felt at ease, understood the man who was talking to them and felt he understood them perfectly. But let us return to his log:

For September 12, 1955:

6 o'clock, partly clear, partly overcast—go shooting—Captain's[6] kitchen garden—miss a rabbit at 40 yards—lift nets with Colin; 1 small skate, 2 redfish, 2 wrasses (pot 1 fine chad and a medium conger) strong north wind. . . .
Evening set 6 snares in Captain's kitchen garden.

[6] The "Captain" was the historian, Charles Seignebos, who was the first person to build a house on the Arcouest headland and whose boat the *Eglantine* every day in summer contained a substantial proportion of the Sorbonne.

On July 6, 1956, Joliot returned to Arcouest for the first time since the death of his wife and noted:

Leave Paris 8:10. . . .
Weather clears up and very fine at Arcouest. Arrive at 17:40. House in perfect order. Dine and listen to radio with Hélène. Euratom business! Must write to Guy Mollet. But is it worth the trouble! I miss Irène very much. Bed at 9:30. Depressed. Go to sleep at 10.

And the last lines in the book, dated Friday September 14, 1956.

Balance sheet: poor weather this summer but very pleased with *Helion*.[7] Excellent lobster catches.

In 1950 in conversation with Michel Rouzé,[8] Joliot drew a self-portrait which will surprise nobody who came into contact with him:

"I was not made to be an intellectual, I have had to learn how to be one. I am little surprised to find myself one of their number. The life I should choose for myself would be in the mountains or as a professional fisherman. I was cut out for that kind of life. I have had to adapt myself to the other. When I have to prepare a speech (I don't say when I have to speak, because speaking impromptu I can manage well enough) I always find it difficult. Preparing fishing nets makes immediate sense to me, it concerns only me. Expressing my ideas to other people risks committing other people. It is a greater responsibility and therefore a greater effort. When I have to write I have terrible trouble in concentrating. Other intellectuals write with facility. If you saw my drafts! On one page only three sentences not crossed out. . . ."

For all those who had the great happiness—if only once—to spend a Sunday afternoon at the Joliots' house at Antony in the Avenue Lenotre, two things are certain. They will remember it with emotion, and they will have the feeling that they alone really knew and appreciated these two exceptional beings, who were so closely united in life and so prematurely reunited in death.

In the great drawing room—decorated with pictures, busts, Joliot's father's hunting horns and fishing trophies—or on

[7] One of Joliot's boats—another was called *Saint-Just*.
[8] *F. Joliot-Curie* by Michel Rouzé, E. F. R. pp. 51-52.

the grass in the garden, the circle is formed, but everyone comes and goes as he pleases, for the hospitality is so complete and so natural that it is impossible to tell the hosts from the guests. The conversation is animated . . . but if one is objective one should explain that for nine tenths of the time it takes the form of a monologue by Fred Joliot interrupted by brief questions and simple remarks from the others, and that to supply a background of sound Pierre Joliot will have put on a record of Johann Sebastian Bach on his gramophone. Quite often one of the friends present may have had a particularly grave worry during the past few days or may be faced with serious difficulties. A moment will come when quite naturally he finds himself alone with Fred, away from the others. He will not need to explain himself, for Fred with his quite feminine intuition will have sensed his problem and will find the words to relieve his worry, to cheer him up, and to give him fresh courage.

For me the name of Joliot means everything that is implied by the word "friend."

It would need the genius of Montaigne to set down what thirty-eight years lived side by side with him in joy and in sorrow, in times of trial and success have meant in terms of the enrichment of my own life.

But the description of the life and work of Frédéric Joliot which I have attempted will have attained its objective if it has given a glimpse—beyond that of the scientist and the fighter—of a man who was profoundly human and profoundly good.

Paris—Vaumarre—Bligny
1960-1961

SELECTED WRITINGS

Conclusion of Professor Joliot-Curie's Report to the Meeting of Nobel Prize Winners (Lindau), July, 1958

Before I conclude, I should like to pass on to you several of the ideas which have been suggested to me by the conditions of present-day research work.

I have worked in the laboratory for more than thirty years and I have witnessed the transformation, slow at first—but now quite rapid—of the working conditions of those who devote themselves to fundamental research in nuclear physics.

Hardly twenty years ago the "artillery" used to probe atomic nuclei could be contained in a flask with a capacity of a few cubic centimeters. An experiment which produced results of very great importance might only call for a very small amount of space—a few square meters—and compact apparatus. The research worker, whose mentality should, in my opinion, resemble that of an artist, felt himself to be close to the phenomenon he studied. Observation was fairly direct. The research worker could give free rein to his creative originality. Without great cost or risk to his colleagues in the laboratory he could progress by trial and error until he reached his goal. On occasion his imagination took wing—like the poet's—and led him to a discovery.

Fundamental research to some extent possessed that element of craftsmanship which is so favorable to the full development of the personality.

The need to explore matter more and more deeply has led to the invention of more and more technical means—many of which are huge and complex. Within a very short space of time the artillery used for launching projectiles, high voltages, the cyclotron, the betatron, the synchro-cyclotron, large and heavy pieces of apparatus, have taken their places in laboratories. A large technical staff has become indispensable to their operation.

At first sight a modern center for fundamental research

on nuclear physics presents to the untutored eye the appearance of an industrial plant. Does not the research worker run the risk of feeling crushed by this admittedly indispensable battery of vast and weighty machines which cost scores —even hundred of thousands—of francs to run for a few hours? He no longer feels free to proceed by trial and error as before. He feels under a strong obligation to undertake a specific piece of work. Experimenting with little chance of success, just "to see what happens," now presents real difficulties—yet does not a discovery very often come as a surprise?

In this transition from the craftman's scale to the industrial scale it seems to me essential to be aware of these dangers and to find conditions for the utilization of equipment which will not stifle the personality of the researcher. One cannot do original work in chains.

Some Reflections on the Human Value of Science.[1]

This article seeks to do nothing more than to set down some of the ideas that have occurred to me, in the course of my life as a research scientist, about the human value of science and about men's often contradictory attitudes to science.

Much has already been written about the human value of science in all its various aspects, and I personally always have a vivid memory of Paul Langevin's magnificent preface to the collection, *Human Evolution;*[2] Jean Perrin's fine lectures, so rich in ideas and poetry;[3] and the books of my English friend and colleague, J. D. Bernal, *The Social Function of Science* and *The Freedom of Necessity*.

It is impossible for me to mention here all the other writings which have had a profound effect on me, but I will mention two more which I find remarkable. One of them is a little-known essay by Victor Hugo on "Art and Science"

[1] Article published in *La Nef,* No. 2, January, 1957.
[2] *L' Evolution humaine, des origines à nos jours,* preface by Paul Langevin, (Paris: Librairie Aristide Quillet, 1934).
[3] "What Modern Civilization Owes to Disinterested Science"— broadcast talk by Jean Perrin.

and the other is by Louis Pasteur, entitled "For the Future of French Science," published in a collection of which the evocative title is *A la lumière des textes oubliés*.[4]

The work of past ages in the field of ideas is of such magnitude that it surpasses the capacity of one human intelligence. Ignorant of the past, at every moment we re-create—sometimes impoverishing but often enriching—until the correct idea has become so familiar that it then becomes natural and easy for it to pass into common action. Although it is most often the requirements of action which set the problems that thought tries to solve, nevertheless, thought, as Paul Langevin liked to say, "is extraordinarily fertile in creating new possibilities for action . . . no effort of thought is wasted for action." But the time taken for the fertilization to occur between the individual and the outside environment and for the passage from thought to the action of the multitude seems to us to be very slow and unrewarding.

It is important to discover the causes, which are certainly numerous, of these processes, but I do not seek to pursue that study here. At all events I am convinced that these processes are not as slow as they seem, which is certainly not to say that we should not make every effort to speed them up. Examples like those of printing and the reforms introducing compulsory education for all are there to encourage us in these efforts. What benefits might we not expect from reforms which would open wide the doors of the universities to the sons and daughters of industrial workers and peasants! Consider the fact that at the moment only a small percentage of the students at our universities are children of the millions of workers and peasants who make up the great majority of the French nation.

Let us return to the consideration of the speed of the processes envisaged. This depends above all on the time scale that we use. Every individual imagines, in estimating time, a unit which is a very rough average of the length of time it takes to accomplish particularly important tasks he does himself or observes from start to finish. What I mean by "particularly important" is things which one remembers all one's life. This unit of time—a few years—is a relatively small fraction of the average life span of the individual. We

[4] Louis Pasteur, "For the Future of French Science" (1871). Preface by Jacques Nicolle, the series: *A la lumière des textes oubliés* (Paris: Editions raison d'être, 1947).

are now accustomed to periods of this kind with so-called five-year and ten-year plans. Generally we stop there, because man likes to see his efforts crowned. Ten years already represents a large proportion of the length of a human life.

To undertake a task which one will not see completed, which will only benefit one's descendants, is not yet something everyone is capable of.

But if we now consider changes which concern large groups of people, we are obliged, in reckoning time, to choose a unit of greater length, of the order of a generation—let us say thirty years. One should, I believe, choose a unit of this kind in order to appreciate the speed of the processes which concern us. You will now understand why I do not find them as slow as they are generally thought to be, when you observe that hardly 200 generations separate us from prehistory—6,000 years! Two hundred grandfathers between them and us—and the progress accomplished now seems swift.

The great events of history would seem nearer, more accessible to us, if we identified them by the number of generations which separate them from us rather than by dry dates, expressed in years.

This simple calculation makes apparent the extreme youth of thinking humanity and to some extent explains the mistakes it has made and, alas, still makes! But at the degree of maturity to which we may already lay claim, there could be no justification for indulgence toward any repetition of these errors of youth!

The span of a generation is not, in its turn, an adequate unit for measuring the considerable space of time needed for the all-important organic evolution of living creatures. Here one must count in hundreds of thousands of years. But these units of time are equally very small compared with the four or five billion years since the universe took on the aspect which we know today. It now seems possible that at a certain time all the matter in our universe was concentrated into one ball of a prodigious density which grew steadily hotter owing to the liberation of nuclear energy. At a given moment the temperature became such that the ball exploded into countless fragments, which constitute the stars which we observe in the sky today.

As for the length of time for which life may continue to be possible on this planet, one can count it—failing accidents—in hundreds of millions of years. Hydrogen, a constituent of the water which is necessary to life, escapes continually from the earth at a known rate. As a result of this, the immense reserves contained in oceans and rocks are gradually being used up. As we know roughly how great they are, it is possible to estimate how long they will take to be completely exhausted. This can only be a very rough calculation for one would also have to take into account the formation of hydrogen through the transmutation of heavier elements under the action of the various types of cosmic radiation which strike the earth's crust. These types of radiation themselves contain proton nuclei of hydrogen atoms.

What stage of evolution will we have reached in hundreds of millions of years' time, if nothing has previously happened to destroy our species altogether?

I believe such long periods of time can have no meaning for us and it seems to me fruitless to speculate about such a distant future. For are these not, in fact, periods of time thousands of times greater than those which separate us as we are now from the stage of unicellular organisms in the history of our evolution?

If a serious threat to humanity arose on earth well before then, we might be obliged to swarm like bees to a planet of perhaps a very distant star, in order to insure the survival of the human race. No doubt it would not be necessary to wait for such a danger to arise in order to attempt to leave the earth. Are we not forever driven forward by our insatiable curiosity and our thirst for adventure? I am already in the realm of speculation now—but let me continue there for a moment.

In order to ensure the maximum profit from this long voyage, it would be best to put only female passengers on board the rocket, equipping them with a number of phials— the contents of which may be guessed. Indeed one is entitled to presume that, with the rapid advance of science in this field, it would not even be necessary to send female passengers. Ovules, together with the phials, would suffice. It may also have become possible to induce parthenogenesis. But it will still be necessary to include the said phials for the purposes of reproduction during the voyage. Otherwise the population which developed on the new planet would be composed exclusively of women.

But all this is a delicate question. Let us be prudent and return to the first project, which remains within the scope of our present-day knowledge.

If the length of the journey exceeded that of a human-life span it would be judicious to keep in the capsule only offspring of the female sex which, of the two sexes, is the one capable of bearing children. In other words, in the rocket along with the phials, only people indispensable to the continuance of the race would be preserved.

Once the new planet had been reached the first boy to be born would be preserved. As for the developments which would follow . . . I must not anticipate. The women who had arrived as the first inhabitants of the new planet would themselves find the best ways of guaranteeing the future of the race. All I can say is that on this planet it would be difficult to spread the belief that man was created before woman!

. . . Man several hundred generations ago was organically very little different from what he is today. His large brain enabled him to think and speak. He lived with the aid of a few crude tools in fear of a hostile and mysterious world. Doubtless our distant ancestors were mainly preoccupied with their war against animals in order to feed themselves each day. This existence is not very far from that of the wild animals we observe. The bird may sing when it wakes at dawn, but it soon sets out in search for food, and if it stops for a few days it dies.

And is life very different for a large number of people today? Does not the threat of unemployment and starvation still exist in many countries which claim to be models of civilization? But that is by the way.

In his brief moments of security, primitive man found sufficient relaxation to act without any immediate utilitarian preoccupation. Ivory carvings and cave paintings bear witness to an intellectual life of some kind. It was no doubt men who had a mental quality of the same order as these primitive artists who succeeded, by means of observation and experiment, in progressively improving the material conditions of existence of their fellowmen.

But men's minds were dominated by superstition and the fear of invisible forces. The forces of nature were imagined as divinities—all the more powerful because their actions were so much beyond man's strength. This state of affairs continued for very many generations, during which time the fear of the wrath of the gods deprived men of every reason to seek an explanation for external phenomena with a view to mastering and making use of them. This terror was a real moral suffering, to which was added physical suffering, disease, and hunger. A few generations further on, after this somber epoch, the first liberating doctrines of the Greek philosophers and moralists appeared. It was really at this period that science came on the scene. The doctrine of Epicurus, "Epicurean physics," helped to liberate men from the fear of the gods—for faced with the magnitude of the tasks which were theirs, these beings must surely have been indifferent to human concerns. . . .

The more recent history of our society gives incontrovertible proof of all that civilization owes to science. The struggle against disease and famine, the subjugation of natural forces, and the liberating spread of knowledge have won many victories in the best interests of humanity.

In this respect the statistics of human mortality are particularly revealing. I have been able to examine those for a European town from 1591 onward.

During the sixteenth and seventeenth centuries the annual death rate in this town remained at three or four per hundred inhabitants—apart from exceptional periods in 1599, 1626, and 1657. In these years big epidemics caused the rate to increase to 20 or even 30 per cent.

One may infer from this that at times of epidemic, plague, and cholera one third of the population of Europe (which was considerable)—and perhaps of the world—was killed.

Epidemics attacked the rich as well as the poor. Protective measures, with the aid of science, made it possible to nip these great scourges in the bud—at least in a great part of the world.

This victory did not, however, bring to an end the fluctuations in the security of human lives. The statistical curves which trace the variations in collective fear, in important social disturbances, in wars, have roughly the same shape as those of the death rate.

Serious attempts to combat the causes of the new fluctuations only began to be made when the great epidemics had been dealt with.

Unemployment and grinding poverty do not present the same indiscriminate threat as do the plague or cholera. It is probable that if poverty were infectious we should have abolished it by now. . . .

Science is not only capable of increasing the duration of

life. Thanks to the wonderful techniques it has given birth to, it can make men's existence a happier one.

The men who benefit from the results of science at every moment of their lives but who, alas, are also only too often victims of it should be told that the capital of scientific knowledge already acquired is such that it could bring them immense benefits *right now*.

It is at present only a tiny proportion of mankind that benefits initially from new techniques, and in order to appease the appetites of the multitude, this small minority knows how to evoke dazzling forecasts of the marvels which science will make available to *everybody* . . . in the year 2000! The multitude generally only profits from scientific progress after long delays. We already speak of journeys by rocket . . . but how many people now travel by airplane?

The wide publication of the findings of science would permit everyone to claim the benefits of science without delay and resolutely to oppose the perversion of science toward works of destruction and death and selfish profit-seeking.

But would it not be best, as has been suggested, to close the laboratories now and to prevent the scientists from continuing their work—if not to hang them—and to content ourselves with exploiting the wealth of knowledge already acquired?

Nature would sooner or later take it upon herself, if we did so, to give us a brutal proof of the fact that such a course was a mistaken one. It is certain that we should be the victims of still more agonizing difficulties if science did not progress.

Looking to the future we know, for example, that the known sources of energy in the world are rapidly being exhausted. It is important to consider this problem and to carry out research which will produce new ones.

A germ might attack the human species tomorrow and try to destroy us, like other species which have disappeared. There is a certain kind of sea plant which in two years has almost disappeared from all parts of the globe. Its destruction has had important consequences, such as the alteration of the muddy seabed along coasts and a very marked reduction in the catches of fish in coastal waters. This scourge which has struck at a plant might tomorrow attack man.

In order to fight these possible diseases it is necessary for us to accumulate a considerable reserve of scientific knowledge. . . .

It is not simply that would it be madness to seek to put Prometheus in chains once more. We need to be able to apply the scientific method to find solutions to the difficult problems of our existence. . . .

We owe to science, perhaps more than to any other human activity, a sense of the collective effort. The findings of fundamental research, to take only one example, become the common property of scientists all over the world, thanks to the rapid diffusion of scientific information. From this results a fruitful solidarity between the research scientists of different nations.

Every new fact we discover in the laboratory reminds us of the often long list of scientists, dead or living, of whose work our own is but the continuation—and very often a scientist wins fame when he has done no more than add the last touch to the shared work of a whole association of research workers. Thus we are happy to think that our work will be useful to our colleagues in London, New York, Moscow, or elsewhere. For this reason I consider excellent the habit scientists have adopted of entitling their papers: "A Contribution to the Study of. . . ." For it is always a *contribution*—even in the case of the great discoveries which lead to new departures in our knowledge.

Thus, every attempt to limit or stop the spread of scientific information represents an extremely serious threat to the progress of science and to civilization.

Science—and this is one of its greatest virtues—is a fundamental factor for unity among the minds of men all over the world. I do not believe there is any other human activity which so certainly wins agreement among men. Scientific observation is expressed in the same modes of thought, whatever the latitude and longitude. And one can believe that the same would be true of other living inhabitants of our universe, if they exist, however different they may be from us in form, if they are endowed with the ability to think. That is one aspect of the universality of science.

Victor Hugo said:
". . . Science is continually correcting what it has said. Fertile corrections . . . Science is a ladder. . . . Poetry is a winged flight. . . . An artistic masterpiece exists for all time

. . . Dante does not efface Homer."

It is true that the artist's masterpiece has a more immutable character than the scientific creation, but I am convinced that the motives of the artist and the scientist—as well as the qualities of thought and action needed—are the same. Scientific creation at its highest peaks is also a winged flight . . . the artist and the scientist thus join in creating, in all their forms, Beauty and Happiness, without which life would be no more than a series of monotonous actions.

The man of science is like the workmen or the artists who built cathedrals. They contributed to a work which sometimes took several generations to complete, without any diminution of their ardor or their love for the creation which they could never see finished.

What magnificent edifices, what works of art we could achieve with modern techniques if we were willing to undertake work not simply for our own benefit but for that of future generations!

Science gives those who serve her a long perspective. It is a creation to which the scientist contributes each day, without having the vain desire to see the end of it himself.

The benefits which humanity derives at every moment of the day from the collective effort, from the accumulated effects of each individual's effort during the course of his own brief existence exalt our confidence in the ascendancy of man.

[Here follows the passage quoted on page 120.]

In conclusion I should like to affirm my confidence in science and in man. Despite the grave errors which man still commits all too often, I am convinced, like Pierre Curie, that every new conquest of science will ultimately have more good than evil effects.

Scientists are perhaps better able to imagine with confidence the immense happiness which science would bring to all human beings in the world of justice and peace. Yes, it is "glad tidings" which they seek to bring to their fellowmen at every instant—tidings which will forever banish the great scourges and diseases which daily kill men, women, and children—tidings which will reduce to a very short period of time the amount of labor necessary for our survival—tidings which will permit everyone, liberated materially, to give themselves the supreme joy of discovery and creation.

A New Type of Radioactivity[1]

Recently we have shown, using a cloud chamber,[2] that certain light elements (beryllium, boron and aluminum) emit positive electrons when bombarded with α-rays from polonium. According to our interpretation, the emission of positive electrons from Be is due to internal conversion of γ-rays while the positive electrons emitted by B and Al originate from disintegration of the nucleus and accompany the emission of neutrons.

In looking for a more precise description of these emissions we have discovered the following phenomenon:

The emission of positive electrons from certain light elements irradiated by α-rays from polonium persists after the removal of the α-ray source. In the case of boron this effect lasts for more than half an hour. We placed an aluminum foil 1 mm from a source of polonium. The aluminum, having been irradiated for about 10 minutes, was placed on top of a Geiger-Müller counter fitted with an aluminum window 0.07 mm thick. We observed that the foil emitted a radiation whose intensity decreased exponentially with time giving a half-life of 3 minutes 15 seconds. One obtains a similar result with boron and magnesium, but the half-lives are different; 14 minutes in the case of boron and 2 minutes 30 seconds in the case of magnesium.

The intensity of the radiation (measured immediately after irradiation with α-rays) increased with increase of irradiation time, up to a limiting value. Then one has initial intensities of the same order of magnitude for B, Mg and Al, of about 150 counts per minute in the counter if one used a 60 millicurie polonium source.

No effect is observed with the elements H, Li, C, Be, N, O, F, Na, Ca, Ni, Ag.[3] For certain of the elements the effect probably does not occur, while for others the half-life may be too short (for us to record).

---

[1] A note from Mme Irène Curie and M. Frédéric Joliot, communicated by M. Jean Perrin. This note announces the discovery of artificial radioactivity. It appeared in the *Comptes Rendus de l'Académie des Sciences,* under the meeting for January 15th, 1934 (vol 198, p. 254).

[2] *Comptes Rendus,* (1933), **196,** 1885.
Journal de Phys et Rad, (1933), **4,** 494.

[3] This phenomenon therefore cannot be due to contamination by the polonium source (author's note).

Experiments performed in cloud chambers or in the electromagnetic deflection experiments carried out by Thibaud have shown that the radiation emitted by boron and aluminum consists of positive electrons. It is probable that the same is true of the radiation emitted by magnesium.

On introducing copper foils between the counter and the irradiated foil, one finds that the bulk of the radiation is absorbed by 0.88 g/cm² for Al, 0.26 g/cm² for B and Mg which corresponds, assuming the same absorption law which applies to negative electrons, to energies of 2.2 Mev for Al and 0.7 Mev for B and Mg.

When the energy of the α-rays bombarding the aluminum is reduced, the number of positive electrons emitted decreases, but the half-life does not appear to be altered. When the energy of the α-rays is reduced to 1 Mev, hardly any electrons are observed.

These experiments demonstrate the existence of a new type of radioactivity giving rise to positive electrons. We think that the nuclear reaction goes as follows for aluminum:

$$_{13}Al^{27} + {}_2He^4 = {}_{15}P^{30} + {}_0n^1$$

The isotope $_{15}P^{30}$ of phosphorus will be radioactive with a half-life of 3 minutes 15 seconds and emits a positive electron following the reaction:

$$_{15}P^{30} = {}_{14}Si^{30} + e^+$$

An analogous reaction can be envisaged for boron and magnesium, the unstable nuclei being $_7N^{13}$ and $_{14}Si^{27}$. The isotopes $_7N^{13}$, $_{14}Si^{27}$ and $_{15}P^{30}$ can only exist for a short time and this is why we do not observe them in nature.

We consider the following reaction much less probable:

$$_{13}Al^{27} + {}_2He^4 = {}_{14}Si^{30*} + {}_1H^1, \; {}_{14}Si^{30*} = {}_{14}Si^{30} + e^+ + e^-$$

the isotope $_{14}Si^{30*}$ being excited and being de-excited in the course of time, giving up its energy to create an electron pair. One does not observe the emission of negative electrons and theoretically it is very improbable that the energy difference between the electrons is sufficient for the negative ones not to be detected.[4] Also this process presupposes an extraordinarily long lifetime for the excited state with an internal conversion coefficient of unity.

[4] Nedelsky and Oppenheimer, (1933), *Phys. Rev.*, **44**, 948.

To summarize: For the first time it has been possible to make certain atomic nuclei radioactive using an external source. This radioactivity can persist for a measurable time in the absence of the source which excites it.

Long-lived radioactivity, analogous to that which we have observed, no doubt can be produced by bombardment with other particles. No doubt the same radioactive atom could be created by several nuclear reactions. For example, the nucleus $_7N^{13}$, which is radioactive on our hypothesis, could be obtained by bombarding carbon with deuterons, following the emission of a neutron.

Evidence to the Conseil Economique

On Thursday, May 24, 1956, at 10.30 A.M., Professor Joliot-Curie gave evidence to the Working Group for the study of atomic industry at the Conseil Economique. The hearing was presided over by Monsieur Wolff.

In the course of a masterly exposition which lasted more than two hours, Professor Joliot-Curie discussed the problems of the nation's power supply, the conditions for scientific research, and the formation and training of research teams.

Past events and the lessons to be drawn from them, as well as future prospects, were discussed in this internal document. Special exceptional permission for its publication has very kindly been given by the President of the Conseil Economique.

—P.B.

After a brief introduction:

Monsieur Joliot-Curie: Sources of energy may be divided into two categories: those which require raw materials extracted from the earth—coal, oil, uranium, thorium—and those which require none, such as waterfalls and all those which originate directly from the energy of the sun's rays falling upon the earth's surface. The latter are extremely important sources, for they will be available as long as there are sun and water. And we can now predict—though these are only very approximate estimates—that there will be sufficient water on earth for the next 500 million to one billion years.

Before these 500 million or one billion years have elapsed we shall be able to launch rockets capable of reaching planets which are at present too near the sun to be habitable but which will later become so. If it later becomes necessary to go to even more distant planets, planets of stars other than the sun, it will be necessary to send men and women in pairs, so that they can have children on the way. Unless human life has been considerably prolonged by then, the parents will not reach these planets, but the children will.

There is a lesson in this which we may find in science and in all human activities: Do we not undertake tasks which we shall not necessarily see completed? And yet we still work with enthusiasm, in the thought that those who come after us will benefit from our work.

In my opinion we must go very seriously—and at once—into the question of the use of solar energy. There is no doubt that technical research will enable us to make considerable improvements in the processes for the utilization of energy from the sun's rays. It is, I repeat, a problem of the greatest importance and one which ought to be of interest to French industry and to the State's applied research institutes. In short we must test all possible sources of energy and press ahead with research in order to find new ones. It would not be reasonable to regard atomic energy as the only source capable of meeting the considerable increase in the power requirements of this country.

However, we are at present concerned with atomic energy and the possibilities for the development of this type of source.

Let us first of all consider the question of the cost price of the atomic kilowatt hour. You have doubtless heard specialists telling you: "It is more expensive than the thermal kilowatt hour, or the hydroelectric kilowatt hour." It is certainly somewhat more expensive today. But in a field which is developing so quickly we are entitled to believe that in one or two years' time it may well be lower. What we need is energy and it is not so much a question of prices as of the hours of work needed to construct and perfect these sources and of the possibilities of mineral resources and of equipment. . . .

I remember that it was at a meeting here in this very room, just after we had started up ZOE in 1948, that I recalled the emotion we had felt when ZOE began to function. At that time we had foreseen that 20 power stations, each producing 200 to 300 kilowatt hours, would produce as much electricity as was consumed in the whole of France, and that a year's supply of fuel for these twenty stations could be carried by a single goods truck.

When one is considering the cost price of the kilowatt hour there are many factors like this to be considered.

> [*Monsieur Joliot-Curie next examines the relative positions of France and other countries as regards deposits of uranium.*]

I must ask you to forgive me for discussing in this long preamble matters which may no doubt seem to you to be of too general a nature, instead of replying directly to the questions you have asked me to examine.

The problems you have posed show how well informed you are already on these matters—the equipping of the different industries which contribute to atomic installations, the problem of training personnel, the role of the State and the cooperation of industry, the problem of research, the protection of personnel, etc. I would add to them the problem of raw material resources and that of guarantees for export outlets and patents. All these problems are linked together and in order to be in a better position to examine them either singly or together, it helps to know the two broad aspects in which they present themselves to us: on the one hand the laboratory aspect of fundamental and technical research, and on the other hand the industrial aspects of mining and processing raw materials and constructing the appropriate power stations.

> [*Monsieur Joliot-Curie then recalls the history of the discovery of fission and the creation of the C.E.A., the Atomic Energy Commissariat.*]

Despite all these difficulties and thanks to the joint efforts of scientists, technicians, and administrators of all political points of view and of French industry, the first French atomic pile, ZOE, started functioning on December 15, 1948. The contribution this achievement made to the world prestige of this country is well-known; the world press of the period testifies to this. It is also well known how the program fixed in 1946 was successfully fulfilled by the construction of the second pile, P^2, and the first power station at Marcoules. I have thought it might be useful to retrace briefly the state of mind which was prevalent at the time of this first stage.

In this connection, it is instructive to read the first report on the work of the C.E.A. from January 31, 1946, to December 31, 1950. You will find it, gentlemen, a valuable lesson for the future at a time when it has become possible to speak of a new stage in the development of atomic energy: that of the construction of big power stations. This report, of which a considerable number of copies were printed, was parsimoniously distributed after our successors had had the cover stamped at the last moment with the word "confidential" in heavy type. I myself could see nothing in this report which it would be desirable to keep secret and I cannot think that the publishers simply wished to keep secret the efforts and achievements of the pioneers in this field. . . .

At all events I would recommend the members of this Commission to obtain copies of this report from the present Administrator General of the C.E.A.

> [*Monsieur Joliot-Curie picks up the report and shows the title to the President of the Commission, who writes it down.*]

In particular you will find here:

1. The arrangements with industry for the preparation and the acquisition of the raw materials: uranium oxide, heavy water, very pure graphite, etc.—and for the construction of various buildings of machines.

2. The organization within the C.E.A. for the direction of mining research and exploitation—and the first important discoveries of uranium deposits in France.

3. The technical research within the establishment and the financial aid granted to external laboratories of a university type for the development of fundamental research.

4. The creation and training of teams of workers.

5. The protection of personnel, proposed laws controlling the use of artificially radioactive elements in France for the prevention of harmful effects of radiation on living organisms.

6. The recruitment of personnel and financial data.

These are the first solutions which were applied then to the problems which concern you at present. The pioneers who have since been removed from the C.E.A. must be glad to see the work which they started continuing in the best interest of the country. (Although they must regret that the action taken against them should have caused some delays in the completion of the program.) A few months ago I myself had the pleasure of being able to visit the Center for Nuclear Studies at Saclay, after six years' absence. There I saw research workers with abundant material equipment at their disposal, hard at work in the fine buildings, the plans of which were well-known to me. But I know that there is a great deal of work to be done between the drawing up of plans and their realization. I think we laid good foundations for those who followed us. We experienced the most difficult time, when one was beginning virtually from scratch in a country which was painfully getting on its feet again amid the ruins of war. . . .

In the conviction that the material potential of French industry is equal to the efforts which will be called for in order to complete the next stage, I wish to emphasize strongly that success will depend essentially on the attitude and behavior of all those, both in the public and in the private sector, who carry responsibilities in this enterprise, and above all those who are appointed by the government to administrate and direct the C.E.A. Their aim must first and foremost be to provide their country with the sources of atomic energy which are indispensable for the substantial improvement of the welfare of their fellow countrymen. No petty considerations of what school anyone comes from, or of private groups, whether industrial or otherwise, must influence their decisions if it is our goal—as it must be—to realize the full use of the material and human resources of France. This establishment, which is financed by the State, should be managed as if it were a company which must present accounts to its shareholders, a company which must bring them a dividend, which must not go bankrupt. It is not enough for the accounts to be in order and to satisfy the State's auditors: results of all kinds which can be translated into benefits should be offered to the community. In short, this establishment must be run like a company, whose shareholders are the taxpayers —shareholders who must be provided with substantial profits, under pain of going bankrupt. This conception should, besides, be that of all directors of establishments which operate on State subsidies. Among these directors there are at present representatives of the various Corps d'Etat, former pupils of the École Polytechnique. I do not think the training they have received and the established traditions are in general favorable to the success of such enterprises—and in particular the one we are concerned with here. There are certainly exceptions and the record of technicians from this school who have given great service to the State is a glorious one. It is glorious, above all, if one looks at the history of technical and industrial development in the nineteenth century. But it must be recognized that during the first part of this century it is much less so. This is all the more regrettable since this great school doubtless recruits the most gifted students from the lycées. The general teaching at the École Polytechnique is not bad, nor is that of the Écoles d'Application, but the question of finding practical solutions to concrete problems is not given sufficient consideration and positions of responsibility are entrusted to young men who have not come up against real difficulties—the demands of production or the dangers of bankruptcy—and who are ignorant—often because of their social origins—about important human problems. The result of this is a kind of sclerosis which has unfortunate repercussions on the national output. Important reforms are required concerning the training and recruitment of the Corps d'Etat. We should like to see the École Polytechnique once more rendering the great services it has done in the past. But I am now already touching on the problem of the training of teams of workers. . . .

In my opinion the amount of industrial equipment required to carry out the program about which Monsieur Francis Perrin has doubtless spoken in his evidence to you is matched by the potential of French industry. A great effort will be needed, but it is possible. It is only necessary to compare the investment, the raw materials, the equipment, and the number of technical and manual workers required for the atomic energy program with those required for the armaments industry in time of peace and even more in times of conflict, as recently in Indochina and at present in Algeria. The effort required for the atomic energy program is a fraction higher than the latter and, perhaps I may add, more profitable to the country as a whole. The necessary industrial equipment does not simply concern the heavy-chemical, metallurgical, and mechanical industries but also the construction industries for various types of apparatus—instruments for measuring and detecting radiation, generators of projectiles, isotope separators, etc. . . . It is a question of creating an industry of medium size based in particular on the application of electronics. Already several companies of this kind have been formed and are beginning to produce equipment which is suitable for use here and even for export.

This aspect of the problem of industrial equipment gives no cause for worry; there may well be, as in the case of heavy industry, outlets abroad. This question of the possibilities for exports seems to me important and touches on the question of the guarantees afforded by patents. . . .

The inventors have abandoned all their rights in favor of

the State. One of the patents has subsequently been taken out again in common with Great Britain. I do not know what has now become of these patents except that there has been an indiscretion, doubtless on the part of the American press, which has spoken of compensation to the inventors, most likely because the American patents authorities did not wish to recognize our patents. How has the French position been defended in this respect? I do not know. I hope that new patents have been taken out since 1950. There is information to be obtained here which should be of interest to the Conseil Economique.

So far, I have tried to show that the problem of industrial equipment was not, in my opinion, the most difficult to solve. It should not give us cause for alarm, provided those who have a great responsibility in the mission which is entrusted to them give evidence of the attitude I have tried to describe. They should then be able to create the enthusiasm necessary for success in all those who, at every level, whether in the public or the private sector, are working on this project in the national interest.

I come now to the problem of training teams of workers. Here we must guard against making mistakes which would compromise everything. In the present state of French industry great things can be achieved very quickly if the country has sufficient men who are competent and determined to succeed. It is a truism that one must first build with men before building with bricks. In this connection I like to evoke the image of plantations of trees which protect land under cultivation from being eroded by streams of water. It takes years before trees are mature enough to serve this function, and science has not so far found a way of making trees grow more quickly. I recall the following instructive story: Lyautey was making a tour of inspection in Morocco. Seeing the desolate spectacle of a valley ravaged by erosion from streams of water he asked the Water and Forestry officer who was with him how the lands could be saved for cultivation. The officer replied: "If forests are planted on the hillsides these lands will become extremely fertile."

"How long would it take for that to happen?"

"Fifty years," said the officer.

"Then begin tomorrow," replied Lyautey.

There is a good lesson for us in this story. The longer the task will take to be completed, the less we should delay before getting down to it. We should immediately initiate measures to increase the number of men capable of working on the development of atomic energy both in the industrial field and in the field of fundamental scientific research. It takes longer to complete the training necessary for these jobs than it does to build a nuclear reactor.

The training of engineers and personnel of all kinds needed for the building of reactors and the production of nuclear energy can easily be undertaken within the framework of the engineering and technical schools by the creation of specialized sections which would complement the general training now given. The creation of a National Institute which would specialize in this field seems to me a good idea, on condition that it is made absolutely clear that it is intended for training specialist technicians in the fields concerned with the realization of sources of nuclear energy. An Institute of this kind should contain, in addition to the basic general training provided, departments for chemistry, electrical technology, electronics, the application of artificially radioactive elements, and the practice of protection against radiation hazards.

As far as I have been able to discover, I am afraid the proposed National Institute has been given a brief which is too vaguely defined, suggesting, in particular, that the basic teaching of nuclear physics could be carried out there. This would be an unfortunate development, which would tend toward the creation of courses that would compete with those run by the Faculty of Science and the other big schools—without the guarantees and traditions (and there are precious ones, such as that of independence in the face of changes in the political orientation of governments) offered by these bodies. It is therefore necessary to be vigilant with respect to the definition and limitation of the functions of such an Institute, the creation of which has just been considered by the Higher Council for National Education.

I now propose to study the problem of specialists in the fields of research—both fundamental and technical research.

Nobody could deny today that the problems posed by technology and the powerful means that it can put at the disposal of science help to enrich and stimulate fundamental scientific research, but it is also true to say that *almost all the great technical and industrial innovations have originated from the knowledge acquired and the discoveries made in fundamental research laboratories.* In other words, science and technology cross-fertilize one another and a relationship must be set up between them which is stimulating for both. That is why we must take great care in the recruitment and training of research workers in both fields and in the relationship to be established between them. I would normally distinguish between three types of research:

1. The fundamental research which it is virtually essential to pursue in universities, at the C.N.R.S. (Centre National de la Recherche Scientifique), in the big establishments like the Collège de France and the Muséum d'Histoire Naturelle.

2. The applied research carried out in certain university laboratories and at the C.N.R.S.; in the laboratories of the engineering schools; in the semi-public sector, at the O.N.-E.R.A. (Office National des Etudes et Recherches Aeronautiques), the E.D.F. (Electricité de France), the C.N.E.T. (Centre National d'Etude des Télécommunications), and the C.E.A.; in the defense ministries and in certain industrial concerns such as Saint-Gobain, Pechiney, and groups like Electro-Sidérurgie, etc.

3. Industrial research principally carried out by industry itself.

The effectiveness of these three types of research depends on the existence in the greater fields of science and technology of well-equipped laboratories or, better, research institutes, with sufficient teams of competent and well-paid workers.

As far as nuclear physics on the one hand, and atomic energy on the other are concerned, this country possesses a capital of considerable value. This capital is vastly superior to that of the countries which are at present attempting to group together in "Euratom." This situation is due to the great contribution made by France to fundamental discoveries in the fields of radioactivity and nuclear physics, which led to the liberation of atomic energy. The work done in France from 1939 to June, 1940—toward the proof of the possibilities for development of exoenergetic reactions in divergent chains in large masses of uranium subject to bombardment by neutrons and using heavy water as a moderator—placed this country in the front rank at that time. The great loss of headway due to the Occupation was partly reduced from 1946 onward (when the C.E.A. was created), and the starting of ZOE at the end of 1948 gave concrete proof of the great improvement in our situation vis-à-vis the great powers. This result was chiefly obtained thanks to the efforts and abilities of teams of workers coming from fundamental research laboratories, whether they had remained in

France during the war or been associated with Anglo-Canadian research.

The Curie Laboratory and the Radium Institute (then directed by Irène Joliot-Curie), and the Nuclear Physics and Chemistry Laboratories, as well as the Atomic Synthesis Laboratory which I direct at the Collège de France and the C.N.R.S., were the principal sources of the workers for the C.E.A. Many students interested in this field gravitated toward these laboratories, which rapidly became overcrowded from lack of space and equipment—in particular powerful generators of projectiles. These laboratories lacked researchers who were sufficiently experienced to be heads of groups, to direct each of the teams of young workers. This gap was caused by the fact that all the senior and best-trained research workers had been taken on by the C.E.A. in order to start this establishment working and ensure its development. It took from five to seven years' work—not only in the three laboratories I have mentioned, but also in those like the Institut de Recherches Nucléaires which I had created in Strasbourg when I was the director of the C.N.R.S.—before there were heads of research groups of sufficient caliber available. But, I repeat, the shortage of space and the difficulty of recruiting technical assistants because of the very low salaries allocated to them considerably hindered the recruitment of new workers.

Despite these difficulties, our laboratories had considerable prestige abroad. Research workers from many countries came to work with us: at one time there were representatives of seventeen countries working there simultaneously. I remember how American research workers, with whom we got on very well, were sent to us to find out how to make discoveries working with very meager equipment ("with pieces of cardboard" was the somewhat exaggerated expression used).

The President: I myself have a copy of the photograph of the laboratory in which your father-in-law discovered radium: it was a wooden shed.

Monsieur Joliot-Curie: Marie Curie used to say: "Yes, it's true: but if we had had a fine laboratory we should have made more discoveries and our health would have suffered less."

At the moment there are between a hundred and fifty and two hundred researchers working in the university laboratories at Paris, Strasbourg, Grenoble, and Lyon, and at the

Center for Nuclear Studies at Saclay. Many of them are doctors of science. They are carrying out fundamental research on nuclear physics. The public authorities have made grants which will make it possible to build several large generators. But it is really imperative that they go further and provide the buildings and equipment which would permit a great increase in the recruitment of research workers from among university graduates and qualified engineers from the schools.

In order to study these problems a Higher Council for Scientific Research and Technical Progress was set up under the chairmanship of Monsieur Henri Longchambon during the government of Monsieur Mendes-France. An inquiry was made into the training and directing of research scientists and engineers. A first report was published. As far as nuclear physics was concerned—for some unknown reason it was associated with molecular physics—a program of extension was drawn up, which would provide for the training of two hundred and forty researchers and engineers annually by 1965. I do not know how these numbers were arrived at or what trust may be placed in them for the field we are considering. The chairman of the working group which produced these figures is an infra-red specialist, and of the nine members, seven are specialists on molecular physics: the other two are the eminent scientists Messieurs Auger and Francis Perrin, who were doubtless chosen to represent nuclear physics, although the nature of the work they had done in the past and the direction of the laboratories which they have undertaken do not belong directly to the field of nuclear physics. Monsieur Guillaumat, who is one of the other seven members, cannot really be considered to be a specialist either in nuclear physics or in molecular physics. He is a former pupil of the École Polytechnique who has been concerned with studies connected with petroleum. The directors of the two principal nuclear physics laboratories in France have been systematically excluded from this question—as from many others—of commissions concerned with the future of nuclear physics in France. Thus the commission created by the same state secretariat for scientific research under the government of Monsieur Mendes-France in order to study the programmes for the construction of generators of projectiles for nuclear reactions excluded the director of the French laboratory which had built the first generators, including a medium-powered cyclotron, which is still the only one working in this country, for the acceleration of deuteron and alpha particles. Last summer the delegation at the big conference on the peaceful uses of atomic energy organized by the United Nations at Geneva did not include the French specialists on nuclear physics who are internationally the best known. The French delegation even voted against one of these specialists being invited to give one of the big evening lectures, as several foreign countries had proposed. Furthermore it was necessary to visit the foreign pavilions, like that of Great Britain, at the Atomic Energy exhibition in Geneva in order to read the names of certain French scientists, who were among the world scientists who had contributed to the discovery of atomic energy. This is a curious way to serve the prestige of France and to give the country its due in the atomic field.

If I have quoted these examples of discrimination from among many, it is not in order to give vent to vain feelings of rancor but in order to show how political sectarianism and stupid rivalries between schools permit us—to the amazement of some foreign countries—to deprive ourselves of the work of competent people who have already contributed a great deal to their country.

The immediate future of atomic energy in France can only be assured if all witch-hunting is abandoned and all our resources are used to the full.

Let us return more specifically to the need which faces us to increase the recruitment of young research workers in the field of fundamental research. I repeat, the lack of space and equipment and the geographical separation of laboratories in the important Paris area first led me to the idea, when I was High Commissioner for Atomic Energy, of concentrating this type of fundamental research work in one specially reserved part of the Saclay plateau. Existing laboratories, personnel, and equipment would all have been moved there. And the management of this great center would have been the common concern of the Faculty of Science, the Collège de France, and the C.E.A. This administration by these bodies in common seemed to me vital in order to safeguard the independence which is indispensable to fundamental research in the face of changing political forces and the financial interests of groups which have no regard for the national interest. . . .

On the subject of teaching, there is a great deal that could be said and I can only refer to a few aspects of it here.

Far-reaching reforms are certainly called for in teaching at various levels, where true comprehension of fundamental principles is sacrificed to the detailed absorption of facts, which are only too often presented in an unrelated fashion. The requirements of examinations and of overfull syllabuses put a premium on good memory, which deceives the examiner and, more seriously, the candidate himself, who thinks he has understood the subject. One cannot make proper use of what one has not really understood. Revolutionary measures are required, but it is also essential to take account of past experience and not to try to change everything. There are also very fine traditions to be preserved in the teaching we received and which is still being given.

In any case the first matter to be considered is the training of future university teachers. This will call for a rapid and judicious selection from among existing teachers in order to give the best possible training to the next generation. But this takes time; it is another case in which it is necessary to say, "You must start tomorrow."

Meanwhile an effort has been made with the creation of a third cycle of studies, intended for graduates seeking to perfect their knowledge in new or rapidly developing fields. The teachers of these courses are generally researchers who are still young and fully active, and yet have acquired a good deal of experience in their own specialized fields. The organization and selection of teachers for these courses is of great importance and should be done with the type of guarantees a university can provide. It is, in my opinion, university science faculties which should be responsible for this task: let them pick teachers of various origins—university men, qualified engineers, etc. It is essential for research engineers from industry or from public and semi-public establishments to take part in this teaching. It would be very dangerous, in the field of nuclear physics and atomic energy, for the C.E.A. to have sole charge of the organization and selection of teachers—which is the impression that has been given at present. The C.E.A. does not have the necessary qualifications for this: it cannot offer the safeguards which are indispensable to the proper functioning of this third cycle of courses. It naturally should be consulted and should provide some of the teachers from its own staff. The same is true of industries which have research laboratories in which engineers of high quality are working.

The third cycle has begun to function under the aegis of the Faculty of Science and it has made a promising start. In the light of this experience it must now be improved. The numbers needed for fundamental technical research in the atomic field are relatively small compared with those needed in the fields of industrial production and national defense, and there is no cause for alarm. There is sufficient potential to be recruited, given the proper organization. But it should not be thought that at the present time these plans are unrealistic and that it is only by associating our efforts with those of other countries, as is envisaged in the "Euratom" project, that we can increase our forces not only for our own benefit but also (which would be highly desirable) for the benefit of others. I am, in truth, far from being opposed to the principle of associations between countries like this one which aims to set up the European Center for Nuclear Research at Geneva, but it does seem to me essential in the first place for each of the countries wishing to join the association to have made the maximum effort to possess a sufficient national capital—in terms of material and personnel—sufficient scientific and human capital for them to be able to participate usefully in the creation and operation of this international organization *without prejudice to atomic activity on their own soil.* I have on several occasions warned my compatriots of the dangers of the premature creation of such associations with other countries which are often in a worse situation than we are. It is certainly reasonable to envision an association of several countries for the purpose of constructing on a given site a generator of nuclear projectiles more powerful than any which any one of the associate countries by itself could with advantage undertake to build, but we must also be assured that the demand for specialists at the international establishment will not be such that it hinders individual national development. Nor must the nation's contribution to the budget of the international establishment be an excuse for insufficient financing of the national effort. Thus though one may agree with the principle of the European Center for Nuclear Studies at Geneva, it must be recognized that its development is encountering, as I foresaw, serious difficulties over the recruitment of permanent staff. Many of the warmest French supporters of the Center, seeing some of their best colleagues about to leave them for Geneva where the salaries are better, are now trying to stop them from going. . . .

Before concluding this survey, which is, I must repeat, an incomplete one, of the training and education of research workers, I should like to point out that one of the most necessary reforms is that of making higher education *equally* available to the young representatives of every social class and not almost exclusively to the children of the middle class. The statistics of the background of the students at our universities are instructive on this subject. Is not the proportion of sons and daughters of manual workers among students less than 2 per cent? The immense and very rapid development of science in the U.S.S.R. has only been possible because the regime permitted broad recruitment from all classes.

There is another danger which threatens the successful development of nuclear physics and atomic energy in this country. The C.E.A., faced with the need to take on new personnel, has since 1951 proceeded to recruit them directly from among the pupils of the big technical schools and also from among the young graduates of the university science faculties. Shortly after being taken on they have very often been sent abroad, for a training period, particularly in the United States, *without first having had the slightest contact with the French laboratories specializing in nuclear physics and knowing nothing of French industry—in other words without knowing their own country, its faults and its merits.* On their return they had not the slightest interest in what had been done and what was being done elsewhere in France outside the C.E.A., and even there they were interested mainly in what had been done since 1951, and not since its creation in 1946. No one recommended that they make contact with our laboratories—as if a danger of contamination were feared. The knowledge they could have acquired through such contacts would have given them a better impression of their own country in the field of research and invention, instead of their learning to look down on it and to see it only from a foreign point of view which is at odds with our own national temper. Alas! It is not only in the field we are considering today that such deplorable practices have been manifest. Defeatism is widespread; the spirit of resignation is apparent in the governments which have succeeded one another since 1947.

It is time to change our attitude and we must all make the effort to safeguard the existence and the future of our country.

The President: The Recorder, who is unable to be present today, has asked me to make sure you give us your views on two points: safety measures—both for personnel and for the neighboring populations near atomic installations—and the possibilities for the industrial development of the process of fusion which has so far only been set off in the so-called thermonuclear bombs. What stage has been reached in this? Is there any hope of slowing down the reactions which are produced in this process?

Monsieur Joliot-Curie: On the first question, that concerning the protection of personnel and the neighboring populations, my reply is that with our present knowledge and experience acquired at atomic energy installations, we can now provide effective protection from the effects of radiation. Nevertheless an extremely strict working discipline is obligatory and regular medical examinations and blood tests are necessary. Fixed instruments in the rooms and light dose-meters carried by each worker make it possible to measure the doses received. The big installations must have a medical service and specialist doctors, whose job is to insure the protection of the workers, and externally the users of substances emitting radiation must be examined by a works medical department employing competent inspectors.

The President: In the past there have been fatal accidents with radiation.

Monsieur Joliot-Curie: Accidents can certainly still occur among the staff, just as accidents occur in every industry. I think that given the disciplinary measures taken especially in this field, these accidents will be less frequent than in other fields where people are too often careless of danger or insufficiently organized for reasons of economy.

The President: What about the disposal of fission products?

Monsieur Joliot-Curie: Until we know how to make use of the enormous quantities of fission fragments in some new chemistry at very high temperatures, for example, they must be disposed of. One of the best methods we have at present consists in putting them inside thick blocks of cement, which are then sunk in very deep seas. If the corrosion of the block takes more than a hundred years, the dispersal of the fission products due to the opening of the block will be without appreciable danger. After this long period of time there will only be small quantities of radioactive elements which are bound to be long-lived. The fission products of big reactors should in no case be dumped on the surfaces of seas.

Such a practice, which ought to be rigorously forbidden, would risk polluting the surface waters over a great area and making edible fish radioactive—with all the dangerous consequences this could have for fishermen and consumers. A great deal of surveillance will be necessary.

As for the second question, on the hope of being able to utilize for peaceful purposes the processes which occur in the hydrogen bomb, there is not much I can say. Nevertheless past experience shows us that when we have been pessimistic about the possibility of this or that scientific application, research scientists have reached a solution much more quickly than was thought possible. I am sure that it will be the same with nuclear fission, for even though one cannot see the exact path to be followed, if the source of energy exists it should be possible either directly or indirectly to make it usable on a scale which is not catastrophic—with a low yield, but still at a great profit. The use of the energy from the sun's rays falling on the earth may also offer a great profit, despite a low yield. There is nothing more I can say about this subject, except that we must pursue research of all kinds and doubtless a new discovery, made in some fundamental research laboratory, will suddenly permit us to find the technical solution.

Opening Speech at the Peace Congress

Salle Pleyel, Paris, April 20, 1949[1]

I declare the World Congress of the Partisans of Peace open.

Ladies and Gentlemen, Friends,

I am particularly happy to be able to welcome you on behalf of the Preparatory Committee for this Congress which did me the honor on March 18 of electing me president.

I bring you this greeting not only in the name of the Preparatory Committee but also, I am sure, in the name of all those French people—and there are millions of them—who are proud that their capital should have been chosen as a meeting place for those who seek to make an effective defense of that supreme benefit in human life: Peace.

[1] We can only give very short extracts from this introductory report.

The truth to which you will bear witness in the course of our work here will travel invincibly across the world, and will open the eyes of those who do not yet see the dangers which threaten peace. It will unmask the accomplices of war and will cause the immense majority of women and men to act with calm and resolution in order to bar their way. . . .

It is the campaigns of Wrangel, of Denikin, of Weygand, and of Hitler which they want to make us fight again, when they try to convince us—oh, irony!—that we must, in the name of democracy and of liberty (but under the shelter of atomic omnipotence), go out and destroy a regime which has committed the unforgivable crime of abolishing the exploitation of man by man.

In the face of the threats of war which become more specific each day and which are becoming more direct and more pressing, it was high time to speed up the rallying and to coordinate the action of all the forces of progress and peace. We needed to launch a great peace offensive against all the forces of war, and we call this a peace offensive in opposition to those who declare themselves ready to guarantee the peace of the world by dropping atomic bombs.

It is doubtless the first time in history that such a union of human wills has been seen. More than six hundred million women and men from seventy-two countries have given their support to the Congress within a few weeks. And if our most optimistic forecasts have been exceeded, it is because our appeal corresponded to the most heartfelt aspirations of everyone.

Without in any way wishing to prejudice the decisions you will be called upon to take, the Preparatory Committee considered that the following main themes could be debated during the course of the Congress:

1. The denunciation of the arms race,
2. The role of the United Nations Organization in the defense of peace,
3. The denunciation of war propaganda,
4. Respect for the sovereignty and independence of peoples,
5. Economic ties between the nations,
6. The participation of women in the peace movement,
7. The meetings of the Partisans of Peace.

We suggest to you that questions relating to the defense of culture, the problem of colonial wars, and the role of youth in our struggle might also be discussed. . . .

We find ourselves at the dawn of the atomic age, almost in the same situation as the first men who were able to make fire; they used it at first for heat and light and cooking, but their knowledge did not permit them to imagine the steam engine, the locomotive, or the turbine.

How painful it is to realize that if the immense effort devoted to the production and use of atomic bombs for destruction had been directed toward peaceful applications we should already all be able to benefit from them!

It is our duty to condemn these misuses, these perversions of science, and to associate ourselves with the efforts of those who propose that atomic weapons be banned within the framework of general disarmament by the nations.

Scientists faced with their responsibilities cannot remain passive. They rightly believe that the perversions of science can be avoided and many of them are active in this direction. This is, in particular, the case with those who belong to the World Federation of Scientific Workers, of which I have the honor to be president and which has given its enthusiastic support to this Congress.

They do not wish to be the accomplices of those whom a bad social organization permits to exploit the results of their work for selfish and harmful ends. . . .

Among the organizations which are at the origin of this Congress is the Women's International Democratic Federation, which contains tens of millions of members. A great number of other women's organizations have also given us their support.

I want to emphasize the extreme importance of this support. One must not forget that women constitute one-half of mankind and that the evolution of our civilization gives them an increasingly active role in society. Whether it is a question of works of peace or war work, women now participate almost on equal terms with men. During the last war they suffered from the privations more than the men, for apart from their own sufferings they felt deeply the sufferings of their own children.

There are many things which men manage to learn that women already know from instinct—in particular the horror of killing and destroying. They know too well what it costs to create and sustain a human life.

Young people are always the first to be sacrificed in every war, when their lives have hardly begun, lives which they long to fill with happiness and beauty. And those whose lives are spared by the war almost always have their professional training interrupted, an interruption which causes the most harmful disruption of their lives. The last two wars have given us only too many examples of this.

We wish to spare them all such things and we are delighted to find them at our side today and to benefit from the enthusiasm and sincerity of their youth.

We must always remember that apart from the threat of a general war, there are already wars in progress in Greece and in Vietnam and that at every moment men are dying.

The prevention of the coming war, the stopping of the wars now in progress, and the building up of peace—these must be our objectives. . . .

Our desire for peace will not be expressed in a passive pacifism.

To those who still do not perceive the dangers of war, we shall point out what they are.

For those who desire, like us, to defend the peace, we will provide the means.

To those who have understood, but who consciously want war, we say, calmly but resolutely: You will have to reckon with us.

We appeal to all people of goodwill to avoid this scourge of war. Together, conscious of our own strength, we will fight this struggle in the confidence that we shall win.

Message to the Fourteenth Congress of the French Communist Party[1]

> [*Lack of space makes it possible to reproduce only the following short extract from this important message.*]

Permit me now to add one or two remarks about the life of our Party. Despite their simplicity I believe them to be of some importance. I am thinking now of the arguments I have sometimes put forward in the course of many conversations with comrades, or with honest people who do not share our convictions.

[1] The Fourteenth Congress of the French Communist Party took place at Le Havre from July 18 to 21, 1956.

The accession to greater responsibilities in our Party is based on proofs of ability given in action—without forgetting, as one of the criteria for selection, practice in the exercise of leadership which gives a man invaluable experience. It is adherence to these criteria which is responsible for the fact that, taken as a whole, so many of the political lines and actions laid down and applied by our Party have revealed themselves to be undeniably right.

The duty of every Communist is to do everything in his power to further enrich the experience of the Party (and those who direct it). This implies that all militants should take action to insure that praise, criticism, and the resolutions carried by the Party organizations—cells, sections and federations—all come before the leadership. Like any scientific activity, the determination of the Party's policy calls for a precise knowledge of the facts. To avoid making known this praise, this criticism, or these resolutions is to deprive the Party of the knowledge of a part of these essential facts.

Even if they are formulated in an incomplete fashion or are wrong in part, all criticisms or suggestions should be heard with the greatest attention, taking care to distinguish the parts that are right from those which are mistaken. But how much more profitable are criticisms to which proposals for a solution are added! Let us remember, however, that we cannot speak with competence on every subject. Every human being has limitations and it is most particularly in his own field that he should allow himself to formulate criticisms.

Thus is realized within the Party a constant double traffic between the leadership and the base of the Party, the militants. There is no permanent adherence to the decisions taken, for this would negate the effectiveness of all action. There is a close participation by the mass of the Party in the formulation of decisions and a constant adjustment of these in accordance with daily needs, and the difficulties or successes encountered in their application by all the Party organizations.

Sometimes in reading the text of a declaration by the Central Committee, the Political Bureau, the secretariat, or one of the Party leaders I have at first sight been surprised by or even in disagreement with this or that proposition. Knowing the conditions in which the most responsible comrades have acceded to their posts and having verified the correctness of their judgment in many and varied circumstances, I rejected the oversimplified and stupid stance of immediately judging the position adopted to be deplorable. My duty was to look closer and to try to understand the reasons which had made it necessary to adopt this line. This effort generally enabled me to realize that the decisions taken were well-founded. But when I have been unable to discover the reasons behind a decision I have always had a frank and fruitful discussion with the responsible comrades concerned.

Recent events have provoked appeals and invitations on the part of some intellectuals which are sometimes insulting to us. "Free yourselves," they say to the Communist intellectuals, "free yourselves, if only with a cry." But from what are we supposed to free ourselves? I never felt freer in all my life! What freedom is there in yielding to such appeals on the part of those who would be only too pleased to see disunity caused within our ranks.

We certainly must discuss these questions together, seriously and with dignity. There is no denying that there are important and complex problems which cannot be passed over. And I believe that in order to be best equipped to speak of them, we Communist intellectuals must bear constantly in mind the great objectives for which we are fighting, side by side with those who suffer exploitation and the greatest injustices.

As a university man, for example, I can never in these discussions lose sight of the fact that less than 2 per cent of our students come from the working class. The picture of these injustices and inequalities of birth makes it possible to keep a sense of proportion about the time to be devoted to these discussions, whose importance, I repeat, must not be denied, and helps them to take place on a better foundation. . . .

Certainly men are not perfect. Mistakes have been made, some of them very serious ones. Every man must deplore them. And everyone can see how we judge them when they are the work of a man as important as Comrade Stalin. But these are matters which concern neither the doctrine of Marxist Leninism nor the socialist system. They are matters which concern men and one can avoid their repetition by relying on the system and referring to the doctrine. We will thus be able to avoid their happening to us.

This is not an excuse—far from it—but how many crimes are committed, I ask you, each day in the countries which boast of their freedom and which, on the pretext of pacification, for example, kill thousands of human beings?

Letters

TRANSLATION OF A LETTER FROM JOLIOT-CURIE TO LORD RUSSELL[1]

Paris, May 13, 1955

DEAR LORD RUSSELL,

I am very sorry not to have been able to write to you more promptly, as I had promised. Since our meeting in Paris I have had to adhere to a very strict diet, which tires me a great deal, and an attack of influenza has added to my discomforts. I keep to my room in order to avoid complications and have great hopes that I shall soon fully recover my strength.

Although I have been somewhat weakened, the forced isolation in which I find myself for the moment has given me the opportunity to examine in detail certain aspects of the action in which you have invited me and several of our colleagues of various countries to join.

The basis of the personal conversation we had together in Paris was your draft declaration, the draft to which the great Albert Einstein had given his full approval a few days before his death.

In the course of our joint study of this draft you were able to ascertain that I was in agreement with the general ideas expressed. I commented on several expressions which, in my opinion, might risk compromising the noble ideas contained in your draft.

We quickly agreed, at the time of this first conversation, to take note of most of these comments. We both felt how profitable direct contact could be between men who, despite differing political opinions, are profoundly attached to the cause of world peace.

That is why we felt that it would be a good plan to ar-

---

[1] We have selected two of the many letters exchanged between Lord Russell and Frédéric Joliet-Curie: these are reproduced here by permission of Lord Russell.

175

range a first meeting which would make it possible to establish contacts of this kind between people who are experts in their own fields, who command international respect, and who together would represent a broad spectrum of opinions and countries. It is the implementation of this last condition, without any kind of discrimination, which can give every section of world opinion the guarantee that the conclusions reached by these scientists will not have been determined in advance in accordance with a one-sided political bias.

The object of the meeting would be to produce a *reasoned* appeal for an international scientific conference. Provided the unanimous agreement of the scientists present were obtained, this text could be widely circulated.

I believe it would be useful now to return to the draft declaration which you sent to me personally and also to several colleagues, whose names you have given me. In broad outline the argument set out in it is a very valid one and it seems to me correct to say that the objective is an end to wars between all states, whatever they are, given the implicit risk of their extension into world wars. The terrible consequences of the use of atomic weapons (to mention only these and leaving aside, for the moment, other weapons which can doubtless also jeopardize the human race, such as biological weapons) should bring home to everyone the absolute necessity of settling differences between states by means of negotiation, however difficult and slow this may be, and *not by war.* But one of the frequent causes of conflict is interference by one state or group of states in the internal affairs of another. Since the internal affairs of the nation in question are the concern of its citizens, any foreign intervention is, sooner or later, a cause for war between states. Naturally this point of view with regard to problems arising between states or private to a particular state implies the recognition of peaceful coexistence between different social and economic systems. It is opposed to the crusading spirit. A point of view of this kind does not aim to establish a definitive status quo: it would permit social and economic changes within any nation, without armed conflict between states, such changes being in their nature and process the sole concern of the people of this nation. In my own view, to think differently would be to oppose the progress of civilization.

In the new conditions created by the existence of weapons of mass destruction, the chief of which today is the thermonuclear bomb, the need to substitute negotiation for war as a means of settling disputes between states should be better appreciated by all mankind. But it would be very dangerous to believe that the maintaining of stockpiles of atomic and thermonuclear bombs and the continuation of their manufacture are guarantees of peace—and this is also true of the other weapons of mass extermination and the immense stockpiles of so-called conventional weapons, which are continually being manufactured and perfected. The existence of such potential for destruction constitutes a threat at every moment. It can be used by states to put pressure on other states. It is the principal cause of poverty. It creates a dangerous nervous obsession. All this contributes to the maintaining or aggravation of international tension. There is no reason for us to suppose that a government which believed itself to be temporarily in a superior position, thanks to its stockpile of weapons, and thinking that a surprise attack could destroy its enemy, might not unleash a preventive war. To some extent this was the theory of *Blitzkrieg*. We know where this led its exponents and the destruction and death it caused in the world—and in those days the thermonuclear bomb did not exist.

Immediate measures are necessary in order to avoid a cataclysm of this kind. That is why we must campaign for agreements between states to be made as soon as possible, in order to halt the testing and manufacture of atomic bombs of every kind and to utilize the present stores of fissile materials for peaceful purposes.

But what would such agreements be worth if a world war broke out, being fought initially with the immense existing stores of conventional weapons? Within less than a year peaceful atomic industry could be converted for the manufacture of atomic weapons.

What we have said concerning a preventive war in which use is made of atomic weapons also applies, to a lesser degree, to so-called conventional weapons. That is why it is necessary at this crucial stage to reach agreements on the abolition of the various atomic weapons within the framework of a considerable general reduction in armaments. It is clear that such agreements imply the setting up of international measures of control. An international agreement on these points seems to me to be necessary, for the existence of these huge stockpiles of weapons of all kinds, the most powerful of them being thermonuclear bombs, and their constant increase, constitute the greatest source of danger at the present moment.

I believe the removal of this immediate source of danger would be of considerable significance. Among its other effects would be the elimination of an enormous amount of unproductive expenditure and the consequent improvement of men's living conditions, the alleviation of international tension, and the creation of a genuine climate for an international détente. But, like you, I think that although such agreements may open the way for peace, they will not suffice to eliminate war between states. Their effect may well be a great reduction in the temptation to settle differences by resorting to war, but it would not be absurd to suppose that a war, though fought at first with very limited weapons, might nevertheless break out, given the way an industrialized state can quickly transform its peacetime industries for military purposes. It could thus escalate into a world war of extermination. It is essential to bring about a situation where war can no longer be used as a means of settling differences which may exist or arise between states. We may therefore agree on this formula: Negotiation must replace the resort to force.

Various forms of international organization and various international procedures can be envisioned, but the making of a choice between these various solutions does not seem to me to come within the framework of the exchange of views we are thinking of. Our role, as men of science, should be to make known the immense dangers to humanity of a war fought with weapons of mass extermination and the immediate need to eliminate them and also to make it understood that the resort to force between states must be finally ruled out.

I thought it might be useful to explain as clearly as possible my ideas about certain important points already made in your letter, which would doubtless, all or in part, be the subject of discussion at the proposed meeting. The experience I have had the opportunity to acquire at international meetings like those of the Atomic Energy Commission to the Security Council of the United Nations and those of the World Peace Council has taught me how important it is to take care to express one's points of view in such a manner as to avoid from the start all confusion, misunderstanding, and suspicion of unspoken reservations. One must be very patient and responsive to everyone's particular preoccupations, provided they are dictated by a genuine concern to find solutions which are acceptable to all parties. It may happen that either the nature of these legitimate preoccupations or the manner of expressing them comes as a surprise, but one must understand that in general they correspond to habits and methods of thought which are of course personal to each one of us, but also derived from the environment in which each of us lives.

It is because I ardently desire, as you do, that a meeting of scientists such as that envisioned should be a success, that I am so concerned to express in precise terms the points of view which seem to me to be fundamental and to try to formulate them in such a manner as to avoid confusion.

I should first of all like to have your opinion on the points I have made in this letter and the way they are expressed. I believe that what I have said generally corresponds to your own views, but it would be useful to have your agreement before going further.

We must certainly proceed swiftly, but also surely.

Dear Lord Russell, please believe that though at this first stage I may give you the impression of acting too slowly, it is really because I believe it essential to establish a firm basis for our action, which will, I am certain, enable us to save much time later on.

Allow me, therefore, to suggest the following procedure:

1. To wait a further fortnight for the replies to your draft declaration. You have doubtless received some already, with or without comments. Now you have mine. I have sent your draft declaration to the three colleagues you mentioned to me.

2. At the end of the period I venture to suggest you could take the step of writing a letter inviting the colleagues to whom you have addressed your draft declaration (whether they have replied favorably or no, or even if they have not replied)[2] to come to a meeting in order to draft jointly an appeal for the convocation of an international scientific conference. This appeal would show the terrible threat to mankind presented by the existence of weapons of mass destruction—the foremost of these being thermonuclear weapons—and the immediate need to abolish them within the

---

[2] One might eventually extend the invitation to a very small number of additional colleagues, for example the Indian biologist, Sokhey, a former deputy director of the World Health Organization.

framework of general disarmament. Finally, and this is a vital point, this appeal should—in view of what I have said—solemnly emphasize that war must from now on be ruled out as a means of resolving differences or conflicts between states.

I think it is very important to make explicit mention of the need to eliminate atomic weapons immediately, so as not to succumb to the fallacious argument of those who see the best guarantee of peace in the existence of stockpiles of thermonuclear bombs.

A deeper examination of these questions would be the province of the international scientific conference but it would only be when we had made the contacts proposed that we could best envision the agenda of this conference.

The appeal would be drafted in such a way that it could be published. Such a text, carrying the signatures *of all the participants*, would by itself have a great effect on public opinion and upon governments.

I beg you once more to forgive me for having taken so long to reply to you.

Yours very sincerely,

FRÉDÉRIC JOLIOT-CURIE

LETTER FROM BERTRAND RUSSELL TO FRÉDÉRIC JOLIOT-CURIE

DEAR PROFESSOR JOLIOT-CURIE,

Thank you for your letter of June 7. Like you, I am exceedingly anxious to avoid a misunderstanding. Indeed one of the things that gave me most pleasure when I received your original letter was the prospect of collaboration between people of differing political opinions.

Your recollections and mine seem to be somewhat at variance as to the sense in which the typescript I originally showed was a "draft." I thought I had made it clear that, as Einstein had died since signing it, I could not make any alteration of substance unless I were prepared to sacrifice his signature. You may remember that we went through my draft sentence by sentence and that I accepted every alteration suggested by you, and that at the end you said, "these alterations are so slight that you can retain Einstein's signature," and I agreed. It is Einstein's death that makes me unwilling to accept any except trivial changes in the draft. You may remember that before I sent the draft to Einstein I had, at your suggestion, conversations with Dr. Burhop in consequence of which I made important changes with a view to conciliating Communist opinion. As these changes satisfied Dr. Burhop, I allowed myself to hope that they would satisfy you.

I am grateful to you for the trouble you have taken in making a modified statement which you can sign. I have compared your statement very carefully with mine and I find four points which raise difficulties:

1. You say that the abolition of nuclear weapons would be good *even* if accompanied by a general reduction of armaments. I do not like the word "even" and some of those who have agreed to sign would certainly withdraw their signature if it remained.

2. You say the abolition of nuclear weapons would diminish international tension and is therefore good. I say it is good *insofar as* it diminishes international tension. I am not at all sure that an agreement to abolish nuclear weapons would diminish tension since each side might suspect the other of infringing it.

3. You have omitted the need for limiting national sovereignty, which to my mind is absolutely essential.

4. You have omitted the statement that we must learn to think in a new way.

One minor point: you have inserted a quotation from Einstein, which is impossible in a statement signed by him.

None of these points, except perhaps the first, would make it impossible for me to sign the statement that you have sent me, but I cannot substitute his statement for mine both because of Einstein and because I have obtained a number of signatures to my statement and cannot begin all over again with a new one.

I think that if it is really impossible for us to agree on a joint statement, the publication of yours and mine simultaneously would perhaps be the best course. I continue to think, however, that failure to agree is exceedingly regrettable. I had hoped to build a bridge between opposing camps and if this proves impossible a large part of the purpose of the statement is lost.

I shall be grateful if you will let me know what you think had better be done in view of the above difficulties.

With cordial good wishes,
Yours sincerely,
BERTRAND RUSSELL

P.S. (*in handwriting*) I agree with you about the importance of a Committee of Initiative, and I should be quite willing to participate in it.

LETTER TO QUEEN ELIZABETH OF BELGIUM[1]

July 13, 1956

MADAME,

You have devoted a part of your life to work inspired by your concern for mankind and for peace. I remember with what emotion the two thousand delegates from all continents welcomed your message to the World Peace Assembly at Helsinki.

I still have vivid memories of your courageous conduct, which was closely associated with that of your noble husband, during the Great War. Both of you symbolized for me, then an adolescent, the patriotism and dignity of invaded Belgium. On August 22, 1914, my brother was wounded and died on Belgian soil in the shooting at Ethe.

After the war I became Marie Curie's assistant and the husband of her daughter, Irène, and I often heard your names mentioned in tones of respect and gratitude by these two exceptional people when they recalled the war. Marie Curie, helped by Irène, had energetically undertaken the task of organizing X-ray examinations of the wounded at the front in order to facilitate the location of projectiles embedded in their bodies. It was doubtless when Irène was engaged on examinations of this kind, notably on the Belgian front near Ypres, that she received the massive doses of X-radiation which were to cause the terrible ravages to which she succumbed a few months ago.

[1] This letter is published by permission of Her Majesty Queen Elizabeth of Belgium, to whom we wish to express our thanks.— P.B.

I have heard my father speak of the war of 1870, when he was in the militia. My mother lived through three wars. She lost sons in war. I have experienced two wars and during the last one I took part in the creation of a great French resistance movement, the Front National. In it I learned to know and love men of all political opinions, in particular, many Communists, all of whom were inspired by the purest patriotism. This experience, added to all that I had already heard, seen and experienced, taught me to hate war still more.

We do not want our children to suffer from war, as we and our parents have suffered from it.

And yet this fearful specter (still more fearful if one thinks of the effects of atomic bombs) does not prevent some people from envisioning a new war, preparing for it—on the pretext of defense—and even unleashing it, while invoking some kind of mission of liberation and progress, which they claim to be their duty.

But as you have so justly written, in the message you addressed to the World Peace Assembly in Helsinki: "It is not enough today to affirm one's attachment to peace in words." There are now very many of us in the world who are determined to campaign for this end with all our intelligence and with all our strength.

By promoting fruitful cultural initiatives you have enabled people from different nations to learn to know and respect one another. Your enlightened knowledge of music unites your name with that of great musicians.

Many memories come to my mind linking you and your husband with eminent scientists, such as Marie Curie, Albert Einstein, and Paul Langevin: in particular, the memory of the way you received the scientists who were invited to Brussels on the occasion of the famous Solvay Congress.

Permit me, Madame, today, on your birthday, to join with all those who send you their respects, good wishes, and compliments.

FRÉDÉRIC JOLIOT-CURIE

Glossary of Scientific Terms

ALPHA PARTICLE: A particle of mass 4 units and charge + 2, it is the nucleus of a helium atom. Alpha particles (α-rays) consist of 2 protons and 2 neutrons and are emitted from the nuclei of certain radioactive elements.

AMPLIFIER: An electronic device using valves (and nowadays transistors) to amplify the small pulse of electric charge from the counter and to record it as a difference of electric potential.

BETA PARTICLE: (β-ray) An elementary particle synonymous with the electron and emitted by certain radioactive nuclei. A negative electron is represented as β− and a positron as β+.

CHAIN REACTION: A reaction, either chemical or nuclear, in which the reaction products are themselves capable of initiating further similar reactions. Thus the rate of reaction increases rapidly until an explosion results unless the reaction products are removed and the reaction stopped by outside intervention.

CLOUD CHAMBER: An apparatus to observe the paths of electrically charged particles traversing the chamber. The trajectories are seen as a trail of condensation droplets in a supersaturated vapour. (See page 27 for description).

COMPTON EFFECT: A change in frequency, and hence in wavelength, of X-rays and γ-rays when scattered (deflected) by atoms. The effect was discovered by the American physicist H. A. Compton in 1923.

CURIE: The quantity of a radioactive element which emits the same amount of radiation per second as 1 gram of radium in equilibrium with its decay products. It corresponds to 3.7×10^{10} nuclei disintegrating per second. One millicurie is one thousandth of a curie: i.e. 3.7×10^7 disintegrations/second.

CYCLOTRON: A machine invented by E. O. Lawrence to accelerate particles to high energies. The ionized particles (protons or deuterons) spiral outward in a fixed magnetic field, gaining energy from passing between two electrodes (dees) carrying an alternating electric potential.

DEUTERIUM: A heavy isotope of hydrogen of mass 2 units (symbol D). Its nucleus is the deuteron.

DEUTERON: A particle of mass 2 units and charge + 1. It consists of one proton and one neutron bound together.

DISINTEGRATION: Radioactive disintegration is the transformation of one nucleus into another nucleus of different charge and/or mass with the emission of particles and radiation.

ELECTRON: An elementary particle carrying a negative charge and having a mass 1840 times less than that of the proton. The unit charge on the electron is 1.6×10^{-19} coulomb. The number and distribution of the electrons around an atom determine the chemical properties of the atom. COMPTON ELECTRONS: An electron ejected from an atom by X-rays or γ-rays in the Compton effect.

ELECTRONVOLT (eV): The unit used for energy measurements with atoms and nuclei. It is the energy gained by an electron (with unit charge) when it moves between two points whose electric potentials differ by 1 volt.

$1 \text{ eV} = 1.6 \times 10^{-12}$ ergs. $1 \text{ MeV} = 10^6$ eV.

GAMMA RAYS (γ-rays): Very penetrating electromagnetic radiation having a very short wavelength. It is similar to X-radiation but of shorter wavelength.

GEIGER-MÜLLER COUNTER: A device to detect and count charged particles that pass through it. It consists of a metal cylinder concentric with a wire held at a high potential and filled with a gas at low pressure. When a charged particle passes through the counter, it ionizes some of the gas molecules, and the ions are attracted to the central wire.

HEAVY WATER: Water in which the hydrogen atoms are replaced by heavy hydrogen (deuterium) atoms. Formula: D_2O.

ION: In a neutral atom the positive charge on the nucleus equals the negative charge due to the electrons. If any atom loses one or more electrons it becomes a positive ion: it has a net positive charge. If it acquires electrons it has an excess of negative charge and is a negative ion. The phenomenon is known as ionization.

IONIZATION CHAMBER: An apparatus to measure the ionization produced by the passage of a charged particle through a volume of gas. The ionization produced increases the conductivity of the gas, and from measurements of this the intensity of the radiation passing through the chamber can be deduced.

ISOTOPE: The chemical identity of an atom is determined by its atomic number, i.e. the number of electrons in the neutral atom, which equals the number of protons in the nucleus. For a particular element the number of protons is fixed, but the number of neutrons in the nucleus can vary. Atoms containing the same number of protons but different numbers of neutrons are called isotopes of that element.

MEAN FREE PATH: The mean or average distance that a particle traverses between collisions in a given material.

MEAN LIFE: The mean lifetime of all the atoms in a radioactive sample. It is related to the half-life:—the time taken for half the atoms in a given sample to disintegrate.

MODERATOR: A material such as graphite or heavy water which is used to slow down the fast neutrons emitted by nuclei undergoing fission in a pile.

MULTIPLICATION FACTOR: The effective number of secondary neutrons emitted during fission of a nucleus following the absorption of a slow neutron.

NEUTRON: An elementary particle with a mass nearly equal to that of the proton and carrying no electric charge. While it is stable when inside the nucleus free neutrons are radioactive and disintegrate into a proton + an electron + a neutrino. DELAYED NEUTRONS: Neutrons emitted by the fission fragments after fission has taken place. FAST NEUTRONS: Neutrons whose energy exceeds 1000 eV. INTERMEDIATE NEUTRONS: Neutrons whose energy is greater than that of thermal neutrons but less than that of the fast neutrons. PROMPT NEUTRONS: Fast neutrons emitted promptly as fission of the nucleus takes place. THERMAL NEUTRONS: Slow neutrons whose energy is similar to that of the thermal motion of atoms (about 0.02 eV at room temperature). It is thermal neutrons which initiate fission of the uranium 235 nucleus.

NUCLEUS: The central core of the atom. It contains nearly all the mass of the atom and is of the order of 10^{-13} cm in diameter. It is built up of protons and neutrons.

PILE: An assembly built up from fissionable material (e.g. uranium, plutonium) interspersed with blocks of a moderator.

POSITRON: A positive electron. An elementary particle having the same mass as the electron but a charge of $+1$ unit.

PROTON: An elementary particle carrying a positive charge of one unit. The proton is the nucleus of the hydrogen atom.

RADIOACTIVITY: The spontaneous disintegration of a nucleus to give a nucleus of different atomic number, and accompanied by the emission of radiation. The emitted radiation consists of γ-rays plus either positively charged particles (α-rays or β^+-rays) or negatively charged particles (β^--rays). RADIOACTIVE SERIES: A series of radioactive elements all originating from the same parent. For instance, uranium (isotope of mass 238) is the parent of 14 radioactive isotopes whose final product nucleus is an isotope of lead of mass 206 which is not radioactive.

TRANSMUTATION: The transformation of one nucleus into a nucleus of different atomic number during radioactive disintegration.

Bibliography

WORKS BY IRÈNE CURIE AND FRÉDÉRIC JOLIOT

Oeuvres Scientifiques Complètes. [1. éd.] Paris, Presses Universitaires de France, 1961.

L'Electron Positif. Paris, Hermann & Cie., 1934.

La Projection de Noyaux Atomiques par un Rayonnement Très Pénétrant; L'Existence du Neutron. Paris, Hermann & Cie., 1932.

Radioactivité Artificielle. Paris, Hermann & Cie., 1935.

"Über die künstliche Herstellung der Radioelemente." *Angewandte Chemie,* Jahrg. 49 (1936), pp. 367-369.

Rede (von) Professor Joliot-Curie auf der Tagung des Weltfriedensrates. Berlin 1.-5. Juli 1952. (Berlin, Deutsches Friedenskomitee, 1952)

WORKS ON FRÉDÉRIC JOLIOT-CURIE

Kuznetzov, Boris Grigor'yevich, *Frédéric Joliot-Curie, ein Gelehrter und Kämpfer für den Frieden.* (Die Übersetzung aus dem Russischen besorgten: Richard Semrau und Jürgen Schnakenburg) Berlin, Kongress-Verlag, 1953.

Rouzé, Michel, *Frédéric Joliot-Curie* (Avec un texte du Professeur Bernal). Paris, Les Editeurs Français Réunis, 1950.

Deutscher Friedensrat. *Wissen und Gewissen: Frédéric Joliot-Curie, ein grosser Sohn des französischen Volkes.* Berlin, 1959.

Index